A
Legacy
of
Love

A LEGACY OF LOVE
Author: Debbie Fuller
Co-Authors: Shawn and Brian Chrisagis

Copyright © 2018-2019 by The Chrisagis Brothers

Published by:
RPJ Legacy Books
An imprint of RPJ & COMPANY, INC.
www.rpjandco.com
Orlando, Florida, U.S.A.

Disclaimer: This is a true family story with an element of fiction. With privacy concerns, some names have been changed. The Tombstone of Anthony DeFilippo no longer has two dates due to space needed to fit Carmella DeFilippo. John Chrisagis changed that because Marguerite had already died before this had taken place. All other events are true.

ISBN-13: 978-1-937770-63-1

Cover and Interior Design by Kathleen Schubitz
Cover images: The Chrisagis Brothers

Printed in the United States of America

A
Legacy
of
Love

Table of Contents

Dedication vii
Introduction 9
Meet Nick Clarity 11
Date Night 13
The Search for Anthony DeFilippo 17
St. Lucy's Church 23
Mimi's Bar 31
Meet the Parents 35
New Addition, A Family Grows 39
Daddy and His Little Tony 43
Into Each Life a Little Rain Must Fall 45
The DeFilippo Flaw 47
DeFilippo Family Dynamic 53
At Father's Request 57
All Grown Up 63
A Little Boy Wounded 67
Lacey's Revelation 73
A Budding Romance 77
Mr. and Mrs. John Chrisagis 81
Blessed with Twins 87
A Thorn in the Flesh 99
Faith in Work Boots 103
Loss Shatters Nick's World 109
The Last Straw 113
As the Boys Grew 119
The Letter 125
Three Healings, Life and Faith Altered 131
A Tombstone with Two Dates Explained 137
Nick's Big Decision 143
Call to Salvation 146
About the Authors 146

DEDICATION

This book "A Legacy of Love" is dedicated to the **Legacy** that God gave us and the four **Treasures** that shaped and molded our lives:

1) Our Mom, Marguerite DeFilippo-Chrisagis
2) Our Dad, John Chrisagis
3) Our Nana, Carmella DeFilippo
4) Our Pap, Anthony DeFilippo

These amazing women and men of God were life-changers to all they came in contact with and most of all to the three of us boys. We Thank the Lord for giving us godly guidance that taught us through example and not just by words.

Special thanks to our big brother Anthony Chrisagis who has been our best friend and greatest big brother we could have ever asked or imagined. You have always given so selflessly and you are filled with amazing wisdom. Thank you for being our role model in life... Mom and Dad are so proud of the man you have become and we are too. We love you.

Thanks to Lynda Sullivan our faithful ministry assistant who always has our backs. We appreciate you more than words.

Kathy Schubitz, thanks for believing in us and our ministry. We are blessed to publish our life story through your anointed book company. Looking forward to a long lasting relationship with more books to build the Kingdom. You ROCK!!!

To our spiritual parents Wayne and Stephanie Boosahda for keeping us strong in the Lord through life's hardest storms. You both are gifts from God and we adore you both!

INTRODUCTION

What are miracles, and can we see them today? Many ask these questions and yet still wonder why we rarely see them anymore. Some would ask for what type of people miracles happen. Are they perfect or are they for folks with frailties and imperfections?

If you think miracles are dead, then you have not heard the story of the DeFilippo and Chrisagis families. Now from all accounts these were average families. They were hard working, like most families, without much that stood out as extraordinary about them at all except the fact that they seemed to move from miracle to miracle.

Now with the teachings heard in the churches today you might think that this family was one who lived without a problem in the world because of their miraculous experiences. Well, the facts bear out that this belief is a fallacy.

Get in the most comfortable chair you own, grab a snack and prepare to enjoy the stories of a series of modern-day miracles and a family journey that will leave a true legacy for years to come.

Chapter 1

Meet Nick Clarity

Nick Clarity is a competitive, energetic, and career-minded young man. He was in his late twenties when he landed his dream job. He became a reporter for the *Greenville Herald.* He dreamed of this job ever since he graduated with a Bachelor of Arts in Journalism from Stony Brook University in New York. In college, he diligently worked on his studies, perfecting his writing skills while expanding his research talent. His part-time job during the summer between his junior and senior school years with the University paper gave him the practical experience that helped him land an internship with a local newspaper, *The Daily Gazette.* He fast-tracked his way to success. He graduated and landed a job with a newspaper as a junior reporter.

Pictured above:
Anthony Chrisagis
Ministry Ordination

This new job gave Nick a great deal more freedom to search out stories. He moved from New York to Ohio to work for *The Times Leader.* Because of his previous position, he received a vast resume of experience. Assignments began coming in; he ran with them showing his editors that he had an aptitude for seeking out information. He possessed a welcoming personality so naturally and without effort, people responded to him favorably. Because he was so approachable people found it easy to share their hearts and thoughts with him. His gift of reporting meant being kept him busy by his editors. He was the paper's "go-to-man" to get any story they needed. He enjoyed his job at the Daily Gazette, but tired of others dictating what he was to write. He wanted the freedom to find and explore stories that he came across on his own. He desired to write stories that mattered to his community, stories about issues that he found important. He wanted time to do in-depth research to develop better stories.

His wealth of experience, married with his independent work ethic, made Nick a perfect fit for the position in Martins Ferry, Ohio with *The Times Leader*. This new position came at a perfect time, as his personal life desperately needed change. The move gave him the change he needed. While in college, Nick thought he had met the love of his life and the two were working toward a life together. He felt ready to settle down with his sweetheart. A short time into the relationship, he learned that she had not been as committed as he had been. She cheated on him with two other guys. In retrospect, Nick noticed that the more serious he became, the more promiscuous she became. Eventually he could no longer take this lopsided relationship and he broke it off. Their breakup was very hard on him and moving to a new city to start a new life gave him a fresh start. It allowed him to put her in the past and move on. When the opportunity with *The Times Leader* came up, it seemed the perfect place to start a new life. Therefore, he embarked on a new adventure to erase his past mistakes, taking his talents, drive and ambition to begin anew.

Nick moved and began work in Yorkville, Ohio, a town close to Martins Ferry. He tossed himself into his work but also into the community. He joined the flag football team that played friendly games in the uptown park the first Saturday of every month. In the summers, he played Ultimate Frisbee with a group of friends he made at the paper. His life was full and good. He developed a good balance between work and life.

Six months into this new chapter of his life, he met Lacey. She fit so well into his life. She loved sports as much as he did. In fact, they met at a hockey game. Immediately, they were inseparable. Lacey was a sweet, old-fashioned girl. As a nurse at the local hospital, she tended each of her patients with love and care. She was a picture-perfect nurse. Nick's life seemed to hold great promise for his future.

Chapter 2

Date Night

Evening quickly fell to close an almost perfect day. Saturday was the day in the week when Nick Clarity took time to relax. As a reporter, his hectic schedule seemed to be ever-changing. He never knew how many hours would be required to get the scoop in order to write his story. He loved his job but needed some down time. One Saturday, all was perfect, that was, until the evening. He spent his Saturday on the golf course. He played the best game of his life. It was so relaxing. He had a date following his golf game.

Pictured above:
The Chrisagis Brothers
"Legends Concert"

Nick had an early dinner with his girlfriend, Lacey. He dated the lovely Lacey for almost six months. They were having so much fun and they worked well together. Lately he wondered if this relationship would last for the long haul. She was a wonderful girl, intelligent, ambitious, funny, and oh, so sweet. She was everything he sought in a young woman. There was only one problem and as time went on Nick found it more and more of a glaring problem. Lacey was a Christian and Nick never had any interest in the things of God. He knew Christians and from his experience, they seemed out of touch with reality. He questioned how any thinking person could believe in God. From his perspective, science and history had already proven that the existence of God was a fallacy. He had not come from a family who went to church. His parents believed in allowing their children to pursue spiritual things on their own, as they grew up. Nick had made his decision and his heart was far from God. His girlfriend, on the other hand, was a true Christian who knew and loved her Lord and Savior. Nick loved Lacey, but he began to wonder how much more of this faith stuff he could tolerate.

On one Saturday evening she took him to a Christian Concert called the Legends of Christian Music, presented by *The Chrisagis Brothers*. *The Chrisagis Brothers* are a famous Christian Duo who are also identical twin brothers. This yearly concert featured Christian artists who were Grammy and Dove Award Winners, whose ministry changed lives throughout the world for Jesus Christ. At this concert many different singers performed their hits from long ago. Lacey had a wonderful time at this event, but Nick could only take so much. About half way through the concert he decided to take a much-needed break. Nick had to get away, so he excused himself and took a walk outside.

The evening air was crisp and cool. In the back yard of a church, he noticed a cemetery. He walked on the winding road through the large graveyard. As he started his walk, he stayed on the road but eventually walked off the trail to read tombstones. As he wandered through the graveyard, he read the names on the stones. The older stones told him more about the people buried beneath than the newer ones. Lost in his thoughts, he wondered about the people whose names he read. Looking at each of the dates, he imagined what their lives would have been like. On each stone, he saw a date that marked the beginning of their time, then a dash, and finally a second date that told the world when they took their last breath.

Nick saw the beginning and the end, but his curiosity about the dash remained. It was the dash that symbolized the life that was lived in-between the beginning and the end. As he day dreamed, he noticed a tombstone that stood out among the others. This was different. It had only a beginning date, a dash, and an end date, but there were two sets of such dates! The second set of dates had a beginning date, a dash, and finally an end date. Why would there be a second set of dates on the same tombstone?

He searched the whole stone to see if another name appeared on it, but the only name that he read was Anthony DeFilippo. How could this be possible? He thought perhaps the stone maker made a mistake but that seemed doubtful. What family would accept such a mistake? He noticed the name Carmella DeFilippo on this same tombstone. Apparently, they were husband and wife. Her stone had the beginning date, the dash and the end date as one would expect. Nothing out of the ordinary appeared on her marker. While he pondered all of this, he realized that a great deal of time had passed, and he had better get back to the concert to keep Lacey happy. Soon he slipped back into his chair beside Lacey in the concert hall, but he could not get the name Anthony DeFilippo and the miraculous tombstone out of his mind.

Later that night, long after his date ended, Nick found himself unable to sleep. His thoughts were consumed with the unconventional tombstone seen earlier that evening. Every other tombstone was the same, but this one stood out like a sore thumb. He could not get this out of his mind, so instead of fighting sleep and getting frustrated he got up and went online to research Anthony DeFilippo.

A few days following the Legends Concert Lacey and Nick met for lunch during their work day. After some small talk, he asked her some questions about her faith and the after-life.

Nick began, "Lacey, can I ask you something?"

"Sure", Lacey responded. "Do you remember the night we went to the Legends Concert and I left for a while because I needed some air?", he asked. She responded, "Yes, I remember."

"Well, while I was outside, I walked through a cemetery that was behind a church where I saw something strange," Nick said.

"Really", Lacey answered with concern. She questioned further, "Did something happen up there?" "No nothing like that, I just noticed something and have been wondering about it," he responded.

"What?", she asked. "I was reading the dates on the tombstones when I decided to walk off the path. I noticed one that did not make any sense. Each tombstone had a name and under the name appeared a beginning date, a dash and an end date. There is a stone in that cemetery with two sets of dates," he explained. Lacey listened to his story intently.

She then responded, "All of them have a birth and a death date. Unless the person shares a stone with a spouse and they have not yet died."

Nick responded, "Yes there were two names on the stone but only one name had the two sets of dates under it."

Then Nick asked, "I was wondering, I know that Christians sometimes keep track of the date that marks the day they were born again. Could that be what the second set of dates refers to on the tombstone?"

She responded, "I really don't think so. When Christians give a date for their spiritual birth that marks their new life in Christ. There would be no death date to go with that." Nick thoughtfully concluded, "It really doesn't make any sense."

Pictured to the right: Anthony and Carmella DeFilippo's Wedding
September 18, 1937. They truly were a perfect couple
in every way. What a legacy of love they gave us.

Chapter 3

The Search for Anthony DeFilippo

Days passed since the Legends concert and Nick still was unable to get Mr. DeFilippo and his strange tombstone out of his mind. He buried himself with work assignments but when he had down time, he Googled for any information on the DeFilippo family. He looked up the name and information about the town in which they lived.

His searching yielded very little information. He hoped for substantially more on Anthony DeFilippo, but he did find an address, a marriage license and a property deed at the courthouse. With this information, he learned that Anthony and Carmella ("Carmie") DeFilippo were husband and wife. He searched the address and discovered that they ran a general store from the address found. Through the census he learned that Anthony worked for the railroads, Carmella ran the family grocery store, and they had one child. On August 26, 1938 a daughter named Marguerite "Margie" was born to them. So far, Nick found nothing that would explain the second dash and dates on the tombstone. This family seemed to be an average one. Nick could not forget the sight at the graveyard and he knew he needed to learn more, so he jotted down the address of the grocery store and the home of the DeFilippos. He tucked it into his pocket and returned to work.

Later that day, he put the address into his GPS and took off on his adventure to learn more. As he pulled up to the house on the corner lot, he slowly got out of his car. The large brick home was landscaped with flowers in the yard. He stood for a few minutes just taking it in when a neighbor walked up to him and stood beside him.

"Hello", the woman said, "You interested in the old DeFilippo place?"

He responded, "Not really, I am not interested in the house. I am interested in the DeFilippo family." Nick introduced himself, "I am Nick Clarity, a reporter with the *Times Leader*. I am working on a story about the DeFilippo Family."

The friendly, energetic lady introduced herself, "I am Gaetana ("Gae") Savarese Davis. I grew up in this neighborhood and was the favorite niece of Carmella DeFilippo. I am the daughter of Francie, Carmie's youngest sister. I loved spending time with Aunt Carmie. She was a second mother to me and reared me. I was closer than a sister with her daughter Margie. We shared the ups and downs of life together. Besides my mother, both were the two greatest role models and teachers to me. I loved them and my mom more than words could describe. Margie taught me about Jesus and always ministered into my life. When my own Mom Francie died, Aunt Carmie became my refuge, my mother, my guide. I miss each of them so much and think of them every day. I also miss Margie's husband Johnny Chrisagis. He was a Prince unlike any other. Many people who marry into a family are welcomed but never really accepted by the family. Johnny was different, he was treated as if he were flesh and blood to all in the family. My brother Frank and him were best of friends, like brothers. Margie married the best, but then again Margie was the best. They were a big part of my heart and I feel such a void since they have all passed. Though I have the hope that I will be with them all again in heaven."

Nick realized that he found a wealth of information in Gae and he asked if she would mind telling him about all she remembered of the DeFilippo family. Thrilled to share stories of her childhood with him, they sat for the rest of the afternoon on her porch talking as Gae served cookies and tea. It was a wonderful day for Nick and for Gae Savarese Davis. She gave him the name of the church the DeFilippos attended. His search then expanded to church records. Because of his extensive conversation with Gae, Nick gleaned a great deal of local history and learned about Carmella and Anthony DeFilippo's beautiful life together.

When Anthony DeFilippo first met Carmella Moscato, he was taken by her beauty inside and out. He was four years older than Carmie. He was a tall, handsome, Italian who looked just like the legendary film actor Errol Flynn. When he met Carmie she worked for her parents Antonio Moscato and Angela La Corte Moscato in their family business. Both parents were strong Catholics who reared their children to honor God. They were from Sicily, Italy and came over on the boat to Ellis Island with their six children to America to live a better life.

They moved to Yorkville, Ohio. Angela became a seamstress who taught her daughter Carmella that important skill.

So, when Anthony came to the house wanting to get fitted for a suit made by Angela, he was actually there to meet Carmella, a beautiful young lady who shined with God's sweet spirit of love and goodness. Every year, Carmie played Mary (the Mother of Jesus) in the Christmas Parade. Her beauty and sweet face made her the best choice in the area.

With Anthony smitten by her, he went in for a fitting and asked for Carmella but instead Angela had Francie, Carmella's younger sister, take care of him. Francie was a feisty character, fun-loving and always the life of any party. In fact, Francie made her own party. She always had a grand time, getting into trouble and always avoiding work. She set her eyes on Anthony and to her he was a tall glass of water and she wanted a taste. She flirted up a storm with Anthony and made him blush three shades of red. She even asked him if he would ever go out with her. He then told her he was there for her sister, Carmella. Francie was upset that this Italian Stallion showed no interest in her but at least he would date her sister and that would keep him in the family. So she called in Carmella. Anthony was dumb-founded as he laid his eyes upon her. She possessed a feminism that begged for a man's tender care. At the same time, he saw a strength that could weather any storm. He knew she could be a life companion who would make an excellent wife. She was tender to soften life, making it sweeter and possessing a strength enough to take it on with purpose. Therefore, he had her fit him for a suit and then asked her out.

Exceedingly shy, Carmella thought for a moment... within seconds Francie shouted out, "Carmie, if you don't take him, I will!!"

Anthony and Carmella both laughed; she then said yes. Carmella's attraction to Anthony was revealed in his hard-working ethic and a young man who appeared quite intelligent, extremely handsome and dressed like a true gentleman. He exuded brilliance despite his lack of schooling. Family matters dictated the course for his life. He grew up in a loving family who struggled with the circumstances

Pictured above: Anthony and Carmella DeFilippo's Wedding Sept 18, 1935. They truly were a perfect couple in every way.

of life. He grew up being the eldest of eight children. When the family fell on hard times, Anthony dropped out of school to work and support the family he loved. From a young age, he learned the value and rewards of hard work. Carmella could very easily put her hand and life into the hands of a man such as Anthony. Her insightfulness revealed that family was of utmost importance to him and no matter what life would bring them. His excellent work ethic would see them through. She knew that whatever he had to do to take care of her would be done.

Anthony and Carmella married in 1935 and soon set out on their own, working hard to build a life together. This couple was no exception to all brides and grooms who shine with hope, promise, and excitement, as they stood on the edge of the future, ready and willing to jump right in it together. Through the eyes of fresh love, they saw only the blessing of their lives together. At the beginning they had no idea how the imperfect world they live in will shape, change, challenge that love, and how situations out of their control will shape their love for years to come. Young and in love, they had maturity that helped them understand that life would be a unique mixture of struggles and blessings all their own. Hand in hand they were both ready to take on whatever life had in store.

As marriage began, Anthony worked for the railroads. Throughout his life, he was a hard-working young man. He dropped out of school and went to work to help support his family. His father became sick, and his mother was busy with his seven younger siblings. He worked hard to help his family so that his brothers and sisters could get their schooling. As a result, the habit of hard work became hard-wired into him from a young age. While Anthony worked the railroad, Carmella busily ran the small general store they owned, located in the downstairs of their house. It was a busy but rewarding life because of the generous heart of the beautiful woman who Anthony married. She had a heart to care for anyone who she found in need. It was common for Anthony to come home and find his dining room table filled with other people. She always cooked extra for those she knew were sick or shut in. Anthony loved the welcoming, loving home that Carmella created for them both. Her kindness brought the couple a wealth of friends in the community. The DeFilippos were cared for as much, if not more, than they cared for those they helped. Her kindness made the store and their home a place where people wanted to be. Her heart brought success to their store as well as their lives. It was a good place to live.

They loved the life they built though struggles existed. It was around the time of the great depression and many people were in need. The DeFilippos helped their neighbors as best they could. So many struggled for the basics but Anthony and Carmella helped to make life better for anyone they could.

Chapter 4

St. Lucy's Church

In Nick's search to learn about the DeFilippo family he seized the opportunity to talk with a young priest, Father Tom. Nick took Lacey with him when he met with Father Tom of St. Lucy's Church. When Nick asked about the DeFilippo Family, Father Tom admitted that he never actually met them, but he had heard stories of these amazing people and their fascinating daughter, Marguerite, who was credited with many miracles. The priest sat for hours with them telling stories of the DeFilippo and Chrisagis families that others had passed down to him.

When the young priest came to this parish following graduation from seminary, he remembered old Father Blossy would regale the priests with stories of the characters that made the town interesting. The old priest felt as if the information he imparted about the townspeople helped the young priest to better understand the people and better serve them. On long evenings after the work day ended, the old priest would share these stories.

Pictured above: Carmella and Anthony DeFilippo creating a new life together.

One story in particular was the day that Carmella came to him and shared what she had been doing. He explained that it is human nature to hang on to what is yours, especially during hard times. Carmella DeFilippo went against the grain of human nature to give when it was hard to give outside the home. Giving for Carmella was first nature to her. She looked beyond herself and trusted her Lord to meet her needs. She held all God gave her with loose hands, knowing that all that she received still His belonged to God and He was free to do with it what He wanted. That is definitely not the popular belief of today, where people give ten percent and the rest is theirs to do with as they please. In Carmella's heart, everything was His to do with it as He pleased.

A few years into their marriage, they noticed a change in the safe peaceful community in which they lived. The town was typically a quiet place with people busy about their business, a place where no one feared danger of any kind. Lately she noticed something was not quite right. She was unable to put her finger on it, but the mood was changing, and not for the better. She could not shake the feeling that trouble was in the air. People always lingered around the store and talked. On the front porch the men would sit while sharing a soda and playing some checkers. They talked about people who had died naturally while others were killed shrouded in mystery. Therefore, she listened and knew she was in a good position to learn more.

She kept her ears to the ground as she worked around the store, to detect whatever she could. It took her a little while to figure out what was going on, but she soon realized that the KKK was responsible for these horrible deaths. She made up her mind that she would help stop the killings. From the rumblings of her customers, she discovered that was the fact of the matter. The KKK or Klu Klux Klan, was a white supremacy group formed after the civil war.

Since the war became a distant memory for most, the KKK's membership had waned, but in the north in the 1920's it gained some popularity. The members of this organization were white men who were pillars of their communities that felt a serious wrong had been committed when Lincoln freed the slaves. These men were out to correct what they felt was a serious injustice the only way they knew. They tortured black people to keep them in what the KKK Members felt was "their place". The freed black was their enemy because they did not want them to be equals or heaven forbid, surpass them in social status. Through intimidation and violence, the KKK were out to keep the black man down in his place. They did this with cowardice. There was no pride in what they were doing as they hid their faces and clothing under white sheets. No one knew them nor could they be identified. These members went out in the dark of the night to burn crosses on the yards of those they wanted to scare. Their destruction had even taken lives in their path of hate. "Now as Father Blossy explained this to us," recalled Father Tom, "Running the grocery store, Carmella had her finger on the pulse of the community and its happenings perhaps more than anyone in town."

The grocery store became a community hang-out as well as a place where people shopped for that all-important gathering of provisions for their families. It was a place where people would sit on the porch, drink a soda, and visit with their neighbors. Because of this, Carmella knew what was going on in their town. In fact, she was very busy running the store. She was also privileged to many secrets that she really did not care to know about. She heard the gossip about Mr. Templeton and his late night stepping out with the widow Smith all behind his wife's back. She knew that Mr. Reiffle had been laid off before his family knew. Some of the situations she learned about were more than concerning, but she knew that she needed to help in some way. Her challenge was to find ideas of how to help. She knew that she just had to do something to improve this situation, to protect her neighbors, and make life better for everyone. A few weeks earlier, she heard Mrs. Geisler and Mrs. Burnett talking one morning while shopping Carmella saw them come in together and she greeted them with her friendly smile. After the social greetings, Mrs. Burnett regaled the two women with a tale about her son coming home and told her of what they saw at Baker's Field just on the outskirts of town.

Mrs. Burnett intently spoke, "A group of boys were outside playing in the evening. You know how the older boys will play

Pictured above:
Carmella was a woman of destiny and a true lady of integrity. She shined as a beacon on a hill to her community and all who knew her.

outside in the summer longer than the little ones who are in for the night when the street lamps and porch lights come on. The boys were out and decided to play capture the flag. They enjoyed this game very much and Baker's Field, as my son tells me, is the perfect place to play because of the foliage and the open areas all around the field. But the other night something happened that has me very concerned. They were walking to the field when they noticed a fire from above the trees and shrubs. The boys saw that and ran towards it to see if anyone was in trouble. As they got closer to the scene, they realized this fire had been set deliberately." Mrs. Burnett went on in almost a whisper. "What my boy described next had the hair standing up on the back of my neck. They saw a big bonfire that had been set by the men who were at this gathering. The boys were wise enough to know that they had come up on a meeting that was very mysterious and meant to stay secret.

Around the large fire were men all covered with white sheets and white pointy hats covering their faces with only holes for their eyes to see through. The only way the boys could tell that they were men was because they heard the male voices singing their songs from under their sheets. The boys hid low in the bushes to find out what was going on. This was unlike anything they had ever seen before. At first, they thought it might be a game, but as they watched and listened, they realized this was no game. The boys heard the hate in their voices as they chanted their beliefs. They appeared to be people of faith as they opened and closed their meetings in prayer. However, the boys heard hate in their voices and words. The boys remained as still as possible to avoid being discovered, but also to clearly hear the words being spoken. The men would repeat "KKK". "

Carmella thought she heard of this before. She remembers it being labeled the Moon Mans Chant. Mrs. Burnett went on, "The boys told me the song they sang. She went on to share the lyrics, "I'm gonna tell you how to keep from getting touched when the Klan is on the prowl. Stay home at night and lock your doors up tight, Don't go outside or else you'll find the crosses-a-burning bright. Now I know you won't believe me, So I am gonna' tell you why The Klu Klux Klan Is going to get you by and by."

The boys said they finished this song and yelled "Kill the blacks!" The boys could not believe their ears. This was no game, nowhere near. These men who hid their identities were intimidating in their costumes and even more so with the harmful words.

Carmella listened intently as this story unfolded. She quickly put two and two together to realize that the conversation she heard in the store made a great deal of sense. There was talk of meetings late at night and she knew the men engaged in this talk. She wondered why, Clinton Herron, the bank's president needed to hold a meeting at night. After all, banking hours were from eight in the morning to five in the evening. Pastor Stu Hutchinson, of the Presbyterian Church did have evening board meetings, but they were usually at the church and adjourned by eight in the evening. Still other men of prominent position in the community were spotted by Carmella to be talking of the strange late night meetings. Carmella knew the rhythm of her town and everything that she saw and heard opposed that rhythm. She knew that every day at dawn she could stand at her window and watch the men hurry off to work. She knew when the daily news arrived on her front porch. Ringing church bells reminded the town that it was noon. Something was seriously wrong. As she pondered these things in her heart, Carmella went about her days in her usual rhythm and watched the storm that seemed to be brewing.

After a long hard day of work, Carmella shared her observations with Anthony. He had been home for a while from working at the railroads. He entered the house through the mud room door habitually. He got so dirty at work that it was against the rules for him to enter through any other door as the mess would otherwise be tracked through the house. Carmie always kept an impeccably clean home and with her busy schedule at the store she did not have time to chase after tracked in dirt every day. Having Anthony use the mud room each day kept the dirt to a minimum. So, she prepared their meals as he cleaned up and after all the chores were completed Carmella shared her concerns with her husband.

As they quietly sat together, she reported all the strange happenings that she pondered in her heart for several weeks. She told him of all the pieces of this unfortunate puzzle that she had already pieced together. They sat and reasoned together trying to figure out this mystery hiding in plain sight for anyone who had eyes to see. Anthony praised his wife's attention to detail and care for others. He went on to ask her to keep her eyes and ears opened to see if she could learn the date of their next meeting. When she learned this information, Anthony went to Baker's Field to see what he could learn firsthand.

A few days later Carmella heard the Mayor and Grant Lewis talking about a meeting at ten o'clock on Tuesday. She relayed this information to Anthony that night at dinner. He told her, since he was on the City Council, that he would attend that meeting on Tuesday evening to see what was going on. Anthony was not naïve when it came to politics. When the Mafia tried to take over the area in the past, he used his influence as a councilman to help fight the crime and corruption.

Tuesday night came, and he headed out. The couple often ended their day with a walk in the cool night air, so it was not unusual for neighbors to see them out strolling on a beautiful evening. She wondered if any of the neighbors would notice her missing from the evening walk. Anthony kissed his wife goodbye and walked into the night. As he got closer to the park, his heart pounded so fast. When he finally made his way to Baker's Field, he proceeded with great caution, in total silence. What he saw so far more than confirmed the story that Mrs. Burnett told his wife. In fact, there was smoke from a fire that lit up the night sky in the far end of the park. He cautiously, quietly approached the fire ever so carefully as he crept along the sides of the fields being oh so quiet to stay hidden behind the shrubs and bushes so as not to be discovered. Sadly, he found the stories that they were hearing to be true. He was successful at not being discovered. Once he gathered all the information that he needed, he snuck out the same way he went into the park.

While Anthony was gone Carmella could not sleep so she sat in the front of their picture window looking for any sign of him. Her heart was racing until she saw him making his way back to their house. She had sat there since he left, watching him walk away until she could no longer see him. Quietly, she sat there praying until she saw him walking towards the house. When she finally saw him walking home, silent tears ran down her face. Tears of relief that he was safe and fear of what he learned at Baker's Field. By the time he came up the walkway she ran to open the door. Relieved to see him safely heading home, she could barely contain her excitement. As he stepped into their yard, she flung the front door open and ran out to hug him. Carmella broke the silence, "What did you see?" They sat on their porch steps while Anthony told her all that he had seen and that he had heard of this group. He explained that they were indeed the Klu Klux Klan.

Carmella asked, "You don't really think that this group will take their hate so far as to hurt innocent people?"

"I would hope not," replied Anthony. He went on. "Now that we know what is going on, we are just going to have to watch and pray to see how this plays out."

Carmella responded, "I guess but you can bet I will keep my eyes and ears open and watch for what is going on." She added, "You do know that if this turns violent, we will need to do something?" She thought aloud, "Maybe I should talk to Pastor Hutchinson, he is a reasonable man."

Anthony responded to that comment with an authoritative "No". He went on, The Klan has a history of harming anyone who calls them out." He demanded," You will say nothing because we don't know all the members of this group."

Carmella responded, "Ok I will not say a word."

Several weeks after Anthony DeFilippo's late night stroll to Baker's Field, the newspaper reported that the body of a black man was found floating in the river. Carmella read the name and she did not know the young man, but she did recognize his address. She remembered that a few days before she heard two men who she suspected were part of the KKK talking in the store and mentioned the address that appeared in the paper. At that moment, Carmella realized that they had in fact stepped up their game, so she needed to do the same. How she wished that she had connected the dots before someone had to die. She promised herself that she would help sound the quiet alarm against the KKK and their evil intent.

When she heard of meetings or heard men speak of an address, she made sure to warn the people. Carmella even housed them in her home until she could get them on the train out of town. She took her concern to the priest and coerced him into helping. She asked him to help protect the black community and encourage them to stay in after dark. Carmella told them to go out in groups, and not to be out at all if possible. She set out to get the job done and save as many of her colored neighbors as possible. Before it was all said and done, this little woman was running her own underground railroad.

Chapter 5

Mimi's Bar

Nick experienced a long day at work and then made his day longer by searching out information concerning Anthony and Carmella DeFilippo. He made a great deal of progress but there were still voids that needed filling. He felt tired and needed a break. He was at the point of almost being too tired to drive, so he decided to stop at a small old bar, called Mimi's. This place had been a fixture in the community for as long as anyone could remember. He heard about it but never stopped in until this night. He thought this would be a good time to check it out. He hoped to rest and grab a quick bite to eat. As Nick walked into the establishment, he sat at the bar and ordered a sandwich with a beer. While he waited for his order he began looking over his notes. It was a quaint old establishment with all the amenities of most bars. There was a pool table with tables and chairs scattered about. That evening the bar was not that busy, so the bartender did not have much to do but talk to the customers who were there. As Nick stayed busy looking over his notes from the day's work, the barkeep started a conversation with him by asking the question, "What are you working on there," he asked.

Nick tiredly responded, "I am a reporter for the *Times Leader* and I am trying to find information on a family who lived in town some time ago." The bartender responded, "My family has lived in this town for many generations. We knew and still know many people in town. Maybe I can help." He asked, "Who are you are looking for?" Nick answered, "Anthony and Carmella DeFilippo." The bartender responded, "I did not know them personally, but the old owner of this bar whose name is Mimi was Carmella's

Pictured to the right: A Lady of Valor and Virtue, Carmella DeFilippo at 19 years old.

nephew, Aurora's son. He told my father stories of them when he bought the bar. And my father told me stories about the DeFilippo family while I was growing up." He went on, "In fact, as the story goes many people in this community owe their lives to them."

Nick asked curiously, "What in the world are you talking about?" The bartender answered, "My grandfather told me stories of how they helped people escape the harm from the KKK." He went on to explain, "Back in the day this part of town looked like little Chicago with a large Mafia influence and to top it off the KKK became very active in this area. It was rather common to find Negros murdered, floating in the river." It was the DeFilippos who took it upon themselves to rescue people before they were harmed. In fact, they used the basement of this very bar to hide their Negro neighbors 'till they could get them to safety on the train out of town. The DeFilippos and Mimi provided provision for the Negros and gave them money when they needed the train fare."

"Really," replied Nick, as he sat intently listening to the story.

The bartender went on, "From the stories I've have heard they were such giving people. The Defilippos were loved by all who had the honor of knowing them. My father often talked with his customers in this bar because he felt it was a part of the town's history that everyone should know. He shared the stories that Mimi told him of the many adventures that the DeFilippos and Mimi had while helping their neighbors. They had passed on long ago but, in this establishment, they are fondly remembered."

Nick added, "I did hear stories from the priest at St. Lucy's Church about the KKK and the DeFilippos."

The bartender then remembered, "In fact, because I was curious from the stories my father told me, so I did attend Carmella's funeral. It was an amazing thing to witness. I remember so many people of color at the visitation; all of them were all there to thank the descendants of Carmella and Anthony DeFilippo. They credited Carmella and Anthony with saving their lives and safeguarding their future generations. It was a beautiful thing to see." After getting a bite to eat and talking to the bartender for more than two hours, Nick Clarity continued on his way home. As he drove, he could not help but feel overwhelmed with the stories he had heard. As he pondered them in the dark of the night, how he wished that he had the courage to live and give like the DeFilippos. He also wished he knew them and could learn from them. He wondered how knowing them would alter his life.

Chapter 6

Meet the Parents

Nick and Lacey's relationship slowly and steadily moved toward marriage. With things progressing as they were, the time came for Nick to introduce her to his family. His family was getting together and this seemed the perfect opportunity. Lacey got to meet his parents and his siblings along with their children. Lacey felt more than a little bit nervous about this gathering, but she decided to be herself. She reasoned that if they liked her, they did and if they did not there was nothing she could do about it. If Lacey sensed any dislike, she would take it as a sign that this was not the man God had for her. She knew that a marriage is more than just a covenant between two people. It includes the families of each spouse. Not much can poison a marriage faster than a family who dislikes a new in-law. They can consciously and un-consciously sabotage the marriage.

Lacey's mother had taught her that, telling about when she had fallen in love with a young man and became inseparable. They got along well until she met his family. Nick's parents loved her, but he had a sister who found it hard to like anyone. The young man's parents were tender-hearted people who were rather simple, who lacked the ability to organize the basic demands of life. It was because of this that his eldest sister behaved as the matriarch of the family trying to take care of things for which her parents were unable. From

Pictured to the right, above:
Beautiful young bride Carmella DeFilippo, the epitome of Love.

her years of being in charge she became bossy and because of her youth she lacked a social filter. If she disliked her sibling's prospects for marriage, she immediately let them know how she felt. She had caused such trouble between the two lovers that the relationship fractured and died. His sister's temperament released poison that eventually killed the relationship. Lacey's mother remembered this experience and did her best to warn younger women to look out for red flags in relationships.

Through the years, Lacey found that her mother's advice was sound. She knew that her mother's stories were intended to be lessons that would teach those who had ears to hear. She desired to help others avoid the same mistakes and problems she suffered through. So, they were stories with a purpose for the wise. Lacey had the wisdom to understand that these stories served her as mile markers for the wise to take heed, slow down and examine the direction that she was taking. When Nick and Lacey arrived at the family picnic at his parents' house, the party was in full swing. The adults were busy talking, preparing the spread that all would soon enjoy. Laughter filled the air in the middle of the mountains of work that needed to be done in order to have a successful event. The men fired up the grill and cooled the drinks in the big cooler.

The women marched with a steady parade of dishes ready for the feast, each laying their dish on the table as if they were an offering. The sweet sound of children running around playing filled the air. It was a happy family. Nick introduced Lacey to his parents, Carol and Kevin Clarity. They were warm and inviting people. Nick's mother took Lacey by the arm and introduced her to the rest of the family. With the formalities completed, they spent the rest of the afternoon getting to know one another. Lacey heard silly stories of things that Nick did as a child long before she had known him. They talked of the issues of the day and even family events. While Lacey played badminton with the children Nick and his parents had a quick conversation about her.

Nick asked, "So what do you think?"

They knew exactly what he was asking, and his mother responded, "She is wonderful."

His father added, "She is a sweet girl, who appears to be a good fit for you."

His mother asked, "How serious is this relationship?"

Nick answered, "I love her."

"So, I sense a but, what is the but?" his mother observed.

Nick could never hide anything from his mother. He answered her, "We get along and have fun together. We want the same things, and she is kind." He went on to add, "She is a wonderful girl, but she is a Christian."

Nick's father responded, "Really, I thought you were going to say something such as, she drinks, does drugs, or is a cheater." His mother added, "That's all?" "I know I am picky but sometimes it seems as if we are not on the same page at all", Nick shared. He went on, "It isn't that I hate God, I am just not sure where I stand on the issues of faith. At this stage of my life, it is just not important to me. There will be time for these decisions when I am older, much older. His mother advised, "She is a wonderful girl. My advice to you is to take it slow." She added, "Give it time."

As he watched her play with his nieces and nephews, running around with the wind blowing in her hair and a big smile on her face, he saw a sweet innocence. He thought his parents gave him good advice. He would give it time, as much as he needed to be sure.

Chapter 7

New Addition, A Family Grows

Because of her position at the hospital, Lacey had access to medical records of the DeFilippos and in them she gleaned a lot of information. In those records Nick and Lacey learned of some of the joys and hardships that the DeFilippo family faced over the years. As it goes time moves forward and life changes. One season slides into another... Goals change, relationships change, and as things are added and taken away, life changes.

As time marched on the DeFilippos moved from the honeymoon phase of their lives to a brand new role. In the days when they started on the adventure known as marriage, they were busy learning who they were and how they fit together. They studied each other's temperaments, likes, dislikes and goals.

It didn't take all that long in the scheme of things for the next chapter of their lives together. In the middle of the business of life, working hard to build their lives together and serving others, they were blessed with a baby. They felt ready for a family. As they kept at the work that kept their lives on track it was not long before they were blessed with the news of this new addition to their family. Both were thrilled at the prospect of this new adventure of a little heir to pass on the treasures which God blessed them with. They eagerly awaited teaching their little charge, whether it be a boy or a girl, the values which made their lives sweet. They were about to have a little one for them to share their lives with. Excitement filled the air as they moved into parenthood.

Pictured above:
In 1938 Marguerite DeFilippo was born. She was the prettiest, sweetest, and daintiest little gift from God.

Like most young couples, the prospect of a baby brings excitement like no other event. From the first moment that a young couple learns that they are expecting a baby, life changes, their focus changes. The DeFilippos spent their first years of marriage laying a firm foundation on which to build their remaining years together.

Like most young couples who are expecting a child, the journey seems almost surreal. With moments of wondering, the reality through any physical evidence of the up and coming blessed event remained unseen. Time passed, growth took place and the evidence was unmistakable. Very quickly the waiting that marks the beginning of parenthood is replaced with the all-consuming, busy preparation for the new little person's arrival and the new role that the couple will be taking on. After nine long months the moment for their baby's birth finally arrived. The child decided to make her entrance into the world on the evening of August 26, 1938. Anthony came home that night, after an uneventful day, to find his wife pacing their living room, stopping only to manage the pains of her labor. He knew it was time, so he ran to get the midwife, his sister-in-law, Aurora. They moved her to the bedroom, closing the door on Anthony, but not before instructing him to boil water and find needed things for the baby's birth. After he completed the tasks given to him, he stood alone on the outside.

This whole process from each of their experiences seemed to take an eternity. Her painful labor had her wondering if she would be able to withstand it. As Anthony listened to the sounds of her struggle, it was almost more than he could bear. He wondered if it would ever end. In fear, he cried out to God, praying that it soon would be over and that God would protect his little family. Many tears were shed that night. Tears of pain, tears of worry, and at last, tears of joy. The final tears were sweet and issued as a praise for the gift they had been given. Those tears seemed to wash away the pain and suffering felt during the delivery. Happiness filled the home at the arrival of Marguerite ("Margie") Rose DeFilippo, who was named for her grandmother on the DeFilippo side of the family.

This precious little girl brought great joy to their lives as they watched her grow through each stage of life. In the beginning they spent hours watching their newborn sleep, marveling at the perfection of the little wonder that God and their love placed in their arms. Like all new parents they counted all her fingers and toes and marveled at her perfection. They watched closely the swift changes in growth and development that the infant and toddler months brought and then through the steady slower growth of the school years. They enjoyed every minute with their God-given treasure.

Pictured above:
Sweet little angelic child
Marguerite DeFilippo.
With big beautiful eyes,
her nickname became
Banjo Eyes.

Pictured at right:
Anthony DeFilippo with his precious little girl (Margie).

Chapter 8

Daddy and His Little Tony

The DeFilippo family was a close-knit family. They all worked and played well together truly enjoying each other's company. Mother was kind, caring and nurturing to Marguerite. She worked hard to meet her little girl's needs. She also took the time to teach her lessons which served her throughout her life. At her mother's side is where little Marguerite learned how to be a proper, young, feminine lady. She learned her lessons well, absorbing all her mother had to teach her. Many times, her mother taught by example. Her mother's best lessons were the stories of the Bible. Little Marguerite watched as her mother walked out a deep faith that sustained her in good and bad times. Daily, she saw her mother on her knees in prayer. They prayed together every day.

Marguerite knew the struggles her parents faced. She watched closely to see how they handled hardship while in the Lord's hands. As she grew, she put her hands into the hands of her parents and they taught her to pray. They sought His face for answers to life's challenges. Last but surely not least, because it was Margie's favorite, they would sing hymns from church. Many evenings their neighbors could hear them singing hymns to their Lord while Carmella played the organ. As Margie grew her parents found her to be an easy child to rear. She had a very teachable spirit and a maturity that was beyond her years.

Like many fathers and daughters, Anthony and Margie had a very special relationship. She was his life and he was hers. They always spent as much time together as time allowed. In fact, they spent so much time together that she acquired the nickname "Little Tony" because she was so much like him. Her personality was his, her mannerisms were his, she even looked like him. Margie could read people just as easily as he did. Margie was a loving child with an old soul. She had wisdom beyond her years. She appeared to be angelic and heavenly. Through her eyes, she could see into the soul and felt people's pain. Margie inherited that trait from her dad. Anthony could read people's motives and he always protected Carmella because she ran with her heart to love and help everyone. Anthony and Margie loved taking walks in the evening after dinner. One night late in spring when the day had been hot and the evening cooling beautifully, the sun fell on the horizon as they took one of their walks. The fresh spring foliage ablaze with color presented a picture perfect scene. They both enjoyed the crisp colors, fresh air and the sweet smell of the spring flowers. Marguerite and her father walked along rather quietly as they strolled into the night. She broke the silence by asking her father an important question.

With all the seriousness a young child can muster she asked, "Daddy, how can I repay you for all you have done for me? Your hard work buys our home, our food and our clothing." Margie looked up into her father's eyes and added, "You have done so much for me. How can I ever repay you?"

Listening to his daughter, Anthony swelled in pride of his little angel...but how does he respond to her concern? "Sweetheart, you can pay me back by being a good mother to the children God will bless you with. My Little Tony, you are a gift from God."

"Daddy, you are my gift, too," added Margie, smiling at Anthony with pleasure and joy. As they headed home, both Margie and Anthony thought even more deeply about the great blessings they shared.

Chapter 9

Into Each Life a Little Rain Must Fall

Life is a gift but with the nature of the broken world in which we live, struggles do arise. The DeFilippo's lived through the ups and downs of life. Their biggest struggle came when Marguerite was school age. A tragedy hit that altered each member of the family for the rest of their lives. Their precious little girl had developed a sore throat, which is a common occurrence for most children. Marguerite came home from school looking very tired, pale, and complaining of a sore throat. So sore, in fact, that she struggled to even swallow water. They called the doctor who made a house call to get her treated as soon as possible. Time went on as the entire household focused on Marguerite getting better. They longed to see their energetic, happy little girl again. How they longed for the day when she would once again run and play. Sometimes parents do tire of the energy of the young but when something alters the noise and energy of a child, a parent's world can seem to stand still until that child is restored to normal. So, it was with the DeFilippo family as they longed for her to be healthy and happy.

Unfortunately, it was not to be. The strep throat did not clear up and return a healthy child to their care. As time passed, she improved, but it was not long before things took a grim turn. Marguerite started to have more symptoms such as fever, multiple pains in many of her joints, itchy rash and most concerning were the involuntary muscle movements.

Their doctor explained that

Pictured to the right:
Sweet little Margie plagued with
sickness, yet had a heart for God.

this disease is an inflammatory disease that affects the heart, joints, skin, and brain. When it attacks the heart, the danger produces rheumatic fever that in turn produces antibodies that attack the body's own tissues. In little Marguerite's case, she suffered the heart damage. Her doctor told her parents that she would always need bed rest or even worse, would not survive. Her heart was damaged beyond repair. So too the hearts of her parents were also broken with this diagnosis. They wondered how they would deal with this. What would become of their little girl? How would they deal with it if she died? Their only child could be taken from them way too soon. A parent should never have to bury a child. Both Marguerite's parents made it their mission to keep a close watch, caring for her with the best of their ability. Anthony and Carmella cared for her by placing her in the hands of their loving God, petitioning Him several times daily to spare their child. Ultimately, they trusted that He knew best and would care for them all. Through this dark time this little family drew on their love and faith to see them through. Much more than seeing them through it, their love became stronger. They knew during the storm they were in the very capable hands of their Heavenly Father. Hard times are still to be gone through, not skipped over, but in the hands of God they are more tolerable because one is not walking through any struggle alone. With their Father God's care they were better able to care for their little lady.

Chapter 10

The DeFilippo Flaw

While having a dinner date one evening Nick and Lacey discussed the information they had learned about the DeFilippos. Lacey said, "You know Nick, the more we learn about these people the more I like them. They would be what I would consider dream friends or neighbors."

"I know", said Nick. "At first I didn't think much about it, but they would be the kind of people I would have liked to call friends." He went on, "They just seemed so full of life, caring, and never dull."

Lacey added, "Though there is one thing about their story that has been bothering me."

Nick agreed, "There have been a few things that I have noticed, too."

Lacey went on, "The DeFilippos seemed to be two of the most peaceful, non dramatic people." Nick agreed, "I noticed that too. They never chased drama, but it seemed to chase them, everywhere, at work, in relationships, and in their family." He went on, "It was as if they could never say no to anyone in need."

Lacey said. "So true."

Nick added, "Tommaso Moscato, a nephew of Carmella's...son of her youngest brother Frank...was hired to work in the store to get some pocket money to spend that would give him more freedom from his parents."

Pictured above: Margie at a young age heard the voice of God.

Teenage years seem to be a time of exploring and determining what someone wants to grow into. While still under the covering of their parents, teens have more freedom to learn social standards, how to handle money and who they want to become. They are on the verge of walking into the world to find their unique place. With all the promise of new beginnings, that promise can easily be derailed by the inexperience of youth. Tommaso was almost a man but sheltered so he seemed younger than his age. His innocence made him a target for other young people. He was making poor decisions because of his hunger for peer acceptance and an innocence that put him in danger. Tommaso was a good worker, a sweet kid who always kept busy. He was courteous to his boss and the customers, a real gem. He was the perfect young gentleman who was always on time and proved to be very reliable.

The DeFilippos loved Tommaso and treated him as if he were their own son. So, when they noticed this inexperienced teen happily marching his way into trouble, Anthony jumped in to rescue him. Tommaso had found a group of friends who were less than the best choice for this sweet young man. They were fun, adventurous, and out to make trouble. One day, Tommaso told Anthony that he and his friends were going to hang out at Potter's Field that night. As he told Anthony his plans, Anthony felt uneasiness in his spirit and he warned Tommaso to be careful. The day went on, and all too quickly evening was upon them. Anthony could not forget the discussion he had earlier. He truly felt something was wrong.

Anthony tried to stop Tommaso as he left, and further warned him not to go to Potter's Field. Tommaso did not heed his warning. As the evening progressed Anthony could not get Tommaso out of his mind. Finally, he could no longer take it and he told Carmella the situation and said he was going to take a ride out to Potter's Field. It was a good thing that Anthony followed his intuition. Arriving at Potter's Field, he noticed one lonely person sitting on a big rock. It was Tommaso. His friends convinced him to drink to the point of being drunk. They also left him in the field alone and cold with no way back to town. Anthony took him home where Carmella and he sobered the boy up. She held him tight and then called his parents to tell them that he was safe and receiving care.

Nick continued. "Today I spent time talking to Michele Vinci who lived in the neighborhood all her life. Her father Mike Vinci grew up next to Carmella when she was young. He became a war hero and the families were always very close and respected each other through the years. Michele became a teacher and had Carmella's grandson in school as a student. Michele became like a daughter to Carmella as she got older. Michele told me about an incident that was almost scandalous in the small Yorkville area about Anthony's brother Lorenzo. He was the butcher at Carmella's grocery store. He tried to commit suicide because he was distraught over his wife's overspending. Anthony and Carmella helped him out."

Nick continued the story. "The store employed Lorenzo, who was not only Anthony's brother but the best butcher in the area. He knew his customers so well that he could cut meat to order, knowing what days they shopped and meats they'd request. He diligently prepared for his customers. His goal was to save them time and money, while offering the best quality products. Anyone who knew Lorenzo thought his life was perfect. He was always happy, courteous, fun and organized to perfection. He was the best brother-in-law to Carmella as they worked hand-in-hand together in the store. He acted like a real brother to her. She never needed to worry with him there. In reality, everything but his work life was a frayed mess. Everything spun out of control. The only time Lorenzo felt in control was during his work. He poured all that he was into his work as it gave him a sense of control and well-being. He felt that if this area of his life would be perfect the rest of his personal life would follow suit. As praises for the good job grew, he felt comforted by the fact that he did one thing very well."

"The struggle that Butcher Lorenzo had were not problems of his own doing, but problems created by his wife, Sofia." Nick observed. "Lorenzo was a simple man with simple needs. He was content to have a roof over his head, food in his belly, clothes on his back, and a comfortable bed in which to sleep. He trusted God and felt so grateful for just these things. Lorenzo grew up in poverty and knew what it meant to live without basic needs. He loved his family, a wife, two daughters and a son. He wanted them to all be as happy as he was… by simply just being all together. Unfortunately, Sofia's view of the world differed. She refused to be content with just a roof over her family's heads, food, or the simple comforts in life. Her eyes and heart were set on all the sparkles the world could give. She wanted all she could get her hands on, which amounted to everything she set her eyes upon. Her hunger for material things landed Lorenzo in great debt. He tried to tell her that her over consumption had to stop, but to no avail. His request only prompted tears and yelling. The upheaval was so great that he backed down and left her to her own devises. Unfortunately, as quickly as he brought the money in she spent it. As she persued her desires, he persued an escape. It wasn't that she wanted it all for herself, she wanted everything for her kids as well. She wanted to be envied by all her neighbors.

As the mountain of debt grew, Lorenzo found himself sinking into a deeper depression. He had always believed debt to be a trap to avoid. He was cautious in financial matters and he felt as if his wife's behavior showed him she had no regard for his feelings. Sophia loved Lorenzo but paid no attention that he was dying from all the financial burdens. He eventually succumbed to the desperation and depression that he had let take over his life. As a result, he attempted suicide. It was Anthony and Carmella who brought him back to the land of the living. They found him in their grocery store one evening, lying in a pool of blood. They rushed him to the hospital, and they paid off many of his bills."

Lacey went on, "And we have not even talked about the steady parade of family issues that Carmella's two sisters (Aurora and Francie), brought into their lives with all their needs. The stories I learned about how their families needed help were amazing. One Saturday Carmella received a phone call from the hospital concerning her older sister Aurora who had suffered a severe beating at the hands of her husband Salvatore. The night before, a fight began when he came home drunk. He tired of her asking the same question about where he'd been. When she inquired as to what was taking him away from his family, he became enraged. He knew that he was doing his worst for his family and he could not tolerate the look in Aurora's eyes that spoke louder than any words. It never mattered if she approached him in anger or as level headed as she could be, his response remained the same. His guilt sent him into a downward spiral from which he would not soon, if ever, recover.

Salvatore's marriage to Aurora was arranged by the parents. Aurora, a young teenager only 14 years old, married a man who was 18 years old. Salvatore was head over heels in love with her. In the beginning they were inseparable. They enjoyed being together except she feared his appetite in the bedroom. He kept her barefoot and pregnant throughout most of their early years together. They had eleven children altogether, including four miscarriages.

Her story goes on. As a young man, Salvatore was likeable and outgoing. He was mildly intelligent, but he was a big dreamer, who made up lots of stories. His stories were mostly about how great he was and about fictional things he claimed he did. His personality either made you love him or hate him. He convinced people he was going places, but that was only true because of Aurora being at his side. She was brilliant, hardworking, creative, and loved by all. She was much older than Carmie. She was the go getter, while Carmie was the heart of the sisters, and Francie was the variety and spice of life.

Salvatore and Aurora seemed happy enough until the day he lost his job. At first, he tried diligently to find work. He woke up early every day, out pounding the pavement, inquiring at every business he could find. He left no stone unturned, but he could not get a break. After a while he had lost all hope. With hope out of the picture and his ever-growing need he sought comfort in the only place where it could be found. For Salvatore, alcohol gave him the escape that he needed. He spent so much time at the bars that any money they had coming in would not go to the care of his family but would end up down his throat from a bottle. Salvatore would get so drunk, that he would go home and abuse his wife and seven children. When Carmella found out, she always took the children and Aurora to her home. She tended to their needs. Many times Salvatore would hit Carmella to get to his family, but she stood in the way to protect them all. Anthony didn't like this, so he would have to hit Salvatore and demand him to leave or the Police would be called.

Then Nick added, "I understand the desire to help people but from my vantage point the DeFilippo family had a problem saying no." He asked Lacey, "Is that a Christian thing or something?"

Startled at Nick's question, Lacey continued. "Lacking boundaries is not a Christian thing, it is a human thing." She went on, "Honestly, I know Christians and non-Christians alike who do not have boundaries. Some people want to please people so much they will do anything for others. I believe the issue with the DeFilippos was one of maturity. They were young, and in their inexperience, they wanted to fix whatever they found broken. They did not want to see anyone suffer but they did not have the maturity to understand that people cannot save other people. They lacked the maturity to know when it is best to let others suffer the consequences of their actions. Otherwise they learn nothing and are not motivated to change. Clearly, many of the people in their lives lacked motivation to change because they knew there was a safety net found with Anthony and Carmella.

There are times when the best help is no help at all, especially in the case of someone who keeps repeating the same destructive behavior again and again. The cycle has no chance of being broken without the need." Nick responded, "I think you are right because as they matured, they seemed to know when to help and when to step back. They learned to size up every situation before they acted. They set boundaries with people who protected their priority, their little family."

Chapter 11

DeFilippo Family Dynamic

Anthony and Carmella were the most undramatic people who the Lord had ever put on this earth. They lived in peace with one another and everyone else. Every area of their lives were orderly and very purposeful. They had a plan and were busy working toward it. So, one might ask how in the world did they always seem to fall into drama? They helped people standing on the sidelines as a safety net for those knee-deep in drama. For them, it was easy to approach broken lives who were just acquaintances, but it was a lot harder with family members. Each of them had more than their fair share of family drama. Anthony's family had their dramas and Carmella's sister Aurora, had married a man who had serious problems.

While Aurora ate dinner at their house one evening, one of the children had spilled milk. Salvatore tossed the glass across the room causing it to shatter on the wall. He then picked the child up from his chair by the shirt, smacking him. Carmella could not stand for this, so she grabbed the child out of his hands and set him on the floor. She then stood between the child and

Pictured above: Carmella DeFilippo with her pride and joy, Marguerite.

Salvatore and gave him an ultimatum, "Listen Salvatore if you want to beat someone up pick on someone your own size." She went on, "You beat me if that is what you need to do." Salvatore stood for a few minutes staring into Carmella's eyes as she gave him a stone-cold stare. Her words and stance made him feel as if there was a mirror being held up... A mirror in which he could see the ridiculousness of his actions. He suddenly stopped in his tracks. He simply grabbed his jacket and walked out the door, slamming it as he exited. When the door slammed, Carmella grabbed the chair, which she stood in front of for support as all the strength that she showed Salvatore drained right out of her body. As the children cried in a huddle around her on the kitchen floor, Aurora sat in her chair speechless, still, staring straight ahead. When he would get on the warpath Carmella would take the children to her house to keep them safe and that is what she did that night. When Anthony saw her coming home with seven extra children, he was not happy. It wasn't that he did not want to help but his finances were stretched to the breaking point with their extended family's problems and he knew he could not support any other people.

As Salvatore's behavior worsened, the pressures became more difficult for Aurora. She focused on caring for her seven children. She began to feel very alone in this endeavor. Like her husband, the stress was getting to her, too. Her stress came out in her responses to her husband. She could barely stand to look at him and as she sank further into her own depression, she found him detestable. The worst part of all this was the way Aurora looked at him now. In the beginning, she looked at him with adoration but now when he saw her looking at him, he saw her stress and ever-growing disrespect. She felt that any man who loved his family would take any job to support them, even if he knew that the only job available was below his skill level. As things deteriorated, the only response that Salvatore could manage was one of violence, a very negative and destructive one. He was angry, very angry at the mess his life had become. He had no one to blame but himself, but he was not about to take the blame for anything. It was easier for him to blame his wife, rather than take responsibility. It all finally hit a fevered pitch when he beat his wife, resulting in a visit to the hospital. Her body was not the only thing damaged. Her spirit was equally beaten; she was finally broken.

When the call came, Anthony was at work and Carmella had to get to the hospital to see her sister. Anthony's mother had been staying with them as she was under the weather. Carmella asked her mother-in-law, Margharita Lansalaqua DeFilippo, to watch Margie so she could get to her sister's side. She promised to return quickly. While she was gone, tragedy struck. When she arrived home, she found Margie lying in bed, crying, next to her grandmother, who had unexpectedly died in the bed. The little girl was alone with her when it happened. This experience created a great deal of fear in Margie that haunted her dreams for a lifetime.

Anthony's family had also caused financial stress. They had become accustomed to thinking of him as their provider because that is what he did when they were growing up. So, the pattern continued, and they had always come to him with their needs. Through the years, he paid for their educations, weddings and anything else they needed. It came to the point when Anthony reached the end of himself. He knew the time had come to set boundaries. Anthony and Carmella were so caught up in taking care of other people's families that they failed to notice that they were slowly sacrificing their own. Decisions needed to be made.

Chapter 12

At Father's Request

The last straw came with a request made by Anthony's father, Vincenzo DeFilippo. The granted request derailed the life which they had built. Anthony's sister Martina married a man named Alessandro, who proved to be a large moral problem. His father gave him the unfortunate news that his sister's husband, Alessandro had gotten himself in more trouble than anyone could have imagined.

He was accused of killing a man. Anthony's father had always favored his daughters to his sons. He reared his boys to take responsibility for their actions and take care of their sisters no matter what. He loved his daughters and as a result, he failed to teach them to deal with any situation, but rather just rescued them out of the scrapes they encountered. He spoiled them and failed to teach them anything that might help them deal with life as an adult. Anthony's father lamented to him that his sister would lose her husband if he were sent to jail. With her husband Alessandro locked up, his sister Martina would have no one to provide for her and her children.

Pictured above:
The loving DeFilippo family.

After fully explaining the situation, Anthony's father told him that he needed to do the right thing for his sister. Anthony felt confused by what his father said. He then got to the point and it became very clear. His father told Anthony that for the good of his family he needed to turn himself in for the murder that his brother-in-law committed. He reasoned that Anthony had no other offenses on his record and the officials would go easier on him than on his sister's husband. Anthony sat shocked in total silence because he really could not believe his ears. He had sacrificed his entire life to help rear his brothers and sisters. He had sacrificed his formal education and his youth. He literally had paid for all their needs, education, weddings and so much more. After this conversation, he felt too angry to respond, and he could not tell Carmella about the conversation.

With the silence that permeated their home for days before he was ready to talk, Carmella knew that something bothered him. So, she decided to break the silence by asking, "Anthony, is something wrong?"

The question was the invitation Anthony needed to share what weighed heavy on his heart. At that point he nearly exploded in his attempt to share with his wife the reasons for his heavy heart. He quietly started to share, "My father had summoned me to a family discussion and I just cannot believe what he asked of me."

Carmella asked with great concern, "What did he ask?"

Anthony sat in his chair looking so frail as he shared, "My sister Martina's husband Alessandro was arrested for murder and Father thought that it would be in the best interest of the entire family if I confess to the murder and go to jail in his place."

Carmella could not believe her ears, so she sat in silent support of her husband. He went on, "How could he even ask such a thing?! I have my family for who I am responsible. How could he ask such a thing?! Carmella, you know I have never really minded the sacrifices I had to make for my family when I was younger. I have always loved them all... Thank God my mom died before this or this would kill her."

Carmella added, "They were blessed to have you to help them

through their hard times."Anthony vented, "I know how important it is to care for family, but this is not the sacrifice that I need to make for my family." He thought out loud, "A request such as this one makes me realize my value to my father." Anthony sat in silence as he struggled to say the next sentence, "I am worth nothing to him."

Carmella added, "I am sorry sweetheart. Sometimes when circumstances force someone to be dependent on someone they fail to see the person who is helping them. The relationship based on dependence can see only the need and not the person who is meeting that need."

"I know", Anthony said sadly, "but if only they could see past the need and know the man who filled the needs. When he treats me this way, I almost feel as if I am not a part of the family but an abused slave."

"I am so sorry," Carmella said, as she stroked his back.

"Dare I say it? I am my family's bank rather than being a son. Carmella, I need to be more than the provider, other than the giver, I need to be his son and their brother."

Carmella stated, "There is no way I will allow you to go to jail for this. I love you." Crying, they sat silently for a while. "Do the right thing for us Anthony." Carmella added.

Anthony responded through tears, "I need to tell my father I cannot do this. First, I have you and Margie to care for but most importantly he is asking way too much." He went on, I need to set boundaries in order to have a relationship with my family. I cannot let them treat me this way anymore."

Carmella asked, "That sounds good but how are you planning to accomplish this?"

Anthony answered, "First, I am going to explain to him how he treats me and how he makes me feel. Then I will say no to his request and explain why".

Carmella responded, "That seems like a sound plan".

He thought aloud, "I will explain that I love them, but I need them to respect me. They need to understand that my time, resources and family are just as important to me as theirs are to them. These crazy demands will stop now, or I will never see them again."

Carmella finished the discussion, "Let's go to bed sweetheart and pray about this. You can talk to your father in the morning."

In the morning after a good night of rest Anthony went to speak with his father. He sat down with his father and explained everything that he shared with Carmie the night before. After listening to his son's concerns his father's response was not good. His concern was only for Anthony's sister and her family. He was very disappointed in Anthony's decision not to help. The meeting left Anthony sad. He realized that his refusal to help his sister would probably be the thing that would cause an unrepairable rift between him and his family. Although he knew he had done the right thing, he determined to face the challenge head on. He knew that he had to do this for the emotional health and well-being of his family and himself.

This confrontation set in motion a series of events that altered Anthony's life. Once he stood up for himself his family turned on him, spreading hateful rumors designed to make him look bad. For the rest of his life he struggled, causing him to question his worth. He could not understand how he could possibly honor his father as the scriptures required. He found the command in more than one place in the Bible, in Exodus, Deuteronomy, Matthew, and Ephesians. He understood the importance because of the number of times it appeared in scripture.

He often pondered how he could honor his father when his father refused to have anything to do with him. He thought back to when he was a child, recalling how easy it was to help his family and how much his mother loved him. Showing respect seemed so easy when they needed him. Things were much more complicated as he grew into adulthood. He had other obligations and needed to set boundaries for his own family to succeed. It needed to be done in order for him to move into an adult relationship with them. However, he knew there was no guarantee it would work out and an adult to adult relationship would grow. Sometimes he longed for a relationship with his father and siblings. Sometimes he prayed and asked God to heal the relationships and other times he asked God to show him how he could honor his father in the situation in which he found himself. Finally, after much asking the Lord answered his concern.

As he prayed, he felt the Lord tell him that he did honor God, His Heavenly Father by working hard to provide for his own family, the ones whom he loved and adored. As an adult he was a productive and respectable man. Most importantly, he harbored no bitterness that could have derailed God's plans for his life. He had set the boundaries and if his family had sought a mature relationship with him, they would have welcomed him into their lives. But without these requirements met they would be the ones responsible for the riff. He found this answer a comfort and he knew he was right with the Lord.

At that same time, Aurora contacted Carmie and told her she had had a nervous break down. The doctors told her the climate in California would offer a better place for living. She said she would go out to California with her husband Salvatore and son Dom to find a new life. This was the only way Salvatore could get a job and start over. Carmie loved and looked up to her sister. She cried about the move. Aurora was like a mother to her when she was young but in these past years it was Carmie who took care of Aurora. Carmie, then said, "What about your other six children? You can't just leave them." Aurora then responded and said, "Can you please take care of them Carm? You are the best mom I know and they adore you. I will send for them when Salvatore and Mimi get jobs out in California. I have no choice."

Carmie said, "I would do it in a heartbeat but I am not sure Anthony will be happy about this."

"Pleeeease!" Aurora begged.

Carmella said, "Yes. I will do it for you." Anthony wasn't thrilled but really had no choice. He loved those precious Piazza children and wanted to make sure they had a normal life. He knew how much Carmie loved Aurora and those children and did not want to be the bad guy in this situation. He wanted Carmie at peace over this life-changing choice and tough situation. So for a few years Anthony and Carmie reared Aurora's family as their own.

Chapter 13

All Grown Up

Margie loved having brothers and sisters in her home. Aurora's youngest son, Riccardo Piazza became very protective over Margie. He protected her all through school with the teenage boys who wanted to get to first base with her. He even took her to her first dance. Anthony and Carmella had a way of treating these young teens with great love. The Piazza teens were funny characters who brought much joy to the household. They loved their Aunt Carmie and treated her as if she were a queen. They respected their Uncle Anthony and did everything to avoid making him mad. Aurora's children cherished the fact that these two people cared enough to help rear them. They no longer lived in fear about being beaten as they were by their drunken father. The years went by and as the normal course of things, seasons pass, one right into the next and before they knew it, Margie was grown and the Piazza clan had gone to live with their parents Aurora and Salvatore in California. Anthony and Carmie were sad to see them go but happy that the Piazza family could start anew again.

It was now time to focus more on Margie. But the little girl who brought them such joy was a beautiful young woman now. Where did the time go? She brought them so much pleasure as they watched her explore the world around her. It was not quite the big wide world but the world that the DeFilippo family had introduced her to. They were unable to provide many things, but they met her basic needs and offered her a good childhood. Now she was no longer a child. She became a young lady. Her health improved but the heart condition left her with lifelong struggles. Her body tired easily.

With Margie now in high school, she enjoyed the broadened

horizons that came with being on the cusp of adulthood. Her experience in school was a positive one. Female classmates liked her. She was beautiful, feminine, sweet, soft-spoken, graceful and held high morals and values. Margie was the epitome of what a lady should be and acted as if she were a debutante of royalty. Not only was she classy but popular with the other girls and equally popular with the boys. She resembled a young Audrey Hepburn and many of the guys were interested in her. Boys made their advances, but she rejected every one of them. She possessed the character to avoid being charmed by a handsome face or flattering words. Margie was a young lady who learned and lived with proper manners. She knew that to please the Lord she loved, she needed to keep herself pure. With this desire in mind she carried herself with a greater maturity than most high school students. She did not accept a variety of dates for she believed that dating had one purpose, which did not include being free on a Saturday night. The purpose of dating served to find a life partner. She knew the characteristics that she wanted in a man. She knew what she was looking for and she knew that developing a lot of different relationships would not accomplish her goal for marriage and family.

Pictured above: Marguerite becomes a classy beauty with style, moral integrity, and great character.

She had to stay the course to get the results that she wanted. She understood that marriage worked best when it was entered in purity. She believed that intimacy was a gift from God that should be in a marriage relationship and she wanted the sacredness of that purity for her life. Margie wanted God's blessing on the most important thing that she would do in her life. She knew she was born to be a wife and mother, a calling she wanted to do correctly. The correct way to do this was by laying a firm foundation. On a mission, Margie let nothing set her off course, not even when she met the young man who would become her husband.

He was from another school and another town called Tiltonsville. He was a very handsome, athletic, and charismatic young man named John Chrisagis. Chrisagis is a Greek name and fit his Adonis mythological looks. She was attracted to him, but she knew that he had the reputation of being a serious playboy. He enjoyed dating lots of girls and was not as particular about who he chose. Because he was so handsome girls would throw themselves at him. All the girls loved him, and he took full advantage of their adoration.

At first his reputation caused Margie to reject his flirtations. This was something that he never experienced. Girls had always given him whatever he desired just to be seen with him. He was the prize and every girl wanted him. So, to find a girl who would not cheapen herself just to be with him was a new experience for him. John had never met anyone like Marguerite and the more she resisted the more attracted to her he became. He was so infatuated with her that no matter where she went, he was there. It really became quite the game for him to get her attention. He sought her out at school and anywhere else that he knew she would be. At first his infatuation was rather funny, but it quickly got annoying as she knew a guy like him did not fit the bill for the man she would marry. She was serious about relationships; he was not.

Chapter 14

A Little Boy Wounded

They say that opposites attract and that seemed to be true in the case of Margie and John. Margie came from a loving family who supported and cherished her for a life time. John's experience was quite the opposite. For him, from the moment of conception, he suffered abuse. His family problems started long before he was born.

His mother Helena Kowalski was a young Polish woman with a checkered past. She found herself in love with a man. As a young woman, she jumped into young adulthood with passion but with lack of reason. She lived for the moment with little or no thought for the future. During her wildest days she met a handsome man who took her breath away.

Pictured above:
Handsome John Jermone Chrisagis catches Marguerite's eye and heart.

She fell head over heels in love with him. He was a sexy romantic Italian. She saw him as almost beautiful with dark wavy hair. He possessed a charm with the art of pleasing a woman. His good looks were topped with an inviting personality. He knew how to flirt and made a girl feel as if she were the only woman in the world. He knew how to read what a woman wanted, treating any of his ladies as if they were queens. He showed her a good time, so it was easy for her to fall for his sugary lines. Having had a great deal of fun together, she began to believe that there was a future for the two of them. When a young lady sees the promise of a future with a young man this is the time that she is most likely to turn over her virtue, feeling the deal is set. She loved him and no doubt he felt the same way. He was a master at romance and in deception to get his innermost desires met.

He was a smooth talker, especially fascinated by his ability to charm young women, wrapping them around his little finger. To Anthony, he treated his ability as a sport. He sweet-talked them and seduced them into believing that no one else existed for him. He would then turn around and dump them when they became too clingy. It was a game that he thoroughly and selfishly enjoyed. His behavior had nothing to do with the women, but all this reminded him of how beautiful he thought he was. These ladies stroked his ego, a favorite part of his character. He was a man without much depth of moral character. The long line of beauties who he had worked his magic on was headed by his wife.

Playboy Anthony Moretti was a married man. One woman who stood at the head of his adoring public for the longest time was committed to him for better or worse. With his propensity to stray, she suffered through a lot of the worst. This woman was his wife. Anthony never kept his marriage a secret. In fact, he used her to

his advantage. He spun quite a tall tale that garnished him sympathy from the women he stepped out with. He realized many women are unable to resist a man who requires care. With their desire to nurture, he was well cared for by his many lovers.

For the first time in her life,

Pictured to left:
John Chrisagis longed for love and fulfillment beyond the material things he had acquired in life.

Helena was in love. No doubt, she had these feelings and hoped they were shared by Mr. Moretti. She found out rather quickly that he did not have the same feelings at all. He tossed her aside, moving on to the next girl, but not before he got her pregnant. Helena he felt used, tossed away as if she were just a piece of old garbage. What was she to do? She was stuck and felt there was nothing that she could do. She tried to get in touch with him, but he refused to return her calls. When she called, he pretended that she had dialed a wrong number. When she tried to talk to him again, Anthony told her he was not interested and demanded her to please stop calling. The reality of the situation hit her like a ton of bricks. She lost her virtue, though tattered as it was, to a man who lived without any moral values at all. Yes, she had been promiscuous and lived her life without thinking about the consequences.

Helena dove into life with reckless abandon. She approached relationships like that too. No one could make her see past the moment at hand to the possibilities of the future she was building. No, she could not see that she was not building at all, but merely falling into her future. She lacked vision of what that future might look like. Now she was pregnant and alone. The future smacked her in the face. She was not prepared for what she was now facing. She had to think past the fun and face her future, one that included a baby she did not want, and Anthony Moretti moved to her past. Her life was a mess and she was the only one to blame. With the future staring her in the face she found herself unable to cope. In her desperation the only thing she thought to do was to get rid of the child. She tried several times to abort the baby but her sisters, Maja and Iga intervened.

About this time she met another man. He was nothing like Anthony Moretti. Demitrius Chrisagis was a tough burley guy who was a plain-looking man. Not the type of man that she would normally have been attracted to, but he expressed interested in her. He was very much in love with her and she grabbed his interest for her own personal gain. She married Demitrius Chrisagis, pretending that the baby she carried was his. It all worked out, though not the way she planned. She just took the first opportunity that presented itself. As a married woman she walked into her new role with a lie at the core of it all. She had no intention of telling her husband or the child of his parentage. By putting the past behind her, she thought this was the best way to make a life for her and the child.

Time passed, and a baby boy was born. His name became John Jerome Chrisagis, the son of Helena and Demitrius Chrisagis. He was their first born with a brother to follow named Spiro Chrisagis in due course. The years passed and life went on as normal. Time does pass but people can become stuck in the spot where loss takes place. That is what Helena found in her life. She was stuck in her love for Anthony and stuck in the forbidden secret that she kept from her family. As often happens, we can walk away from the past but, all too often it follows us into the future. It comes alongside us in guilt, regret, depression and more. For Helena her past made her a callous woman who never dropped her guard or her desire to be in charge. She needed control as her life spun out of control. In trying to be in control she became quite demanding. She developed a thick skin over the years that left her stuck in the hard shell she made for herself.

Her unfortunate circumstances rendered her cold and unable to love anyone else properly. For John, such a mother was hard for him to live with. It seemed from the second he was born she disliked him. According to her, he took her youthful fun away, causing her to marry a man who became a second choice. If she remained honest with herself, he would not have been a choice for her at all. Her resentment of this child altered her life. In her rational mind she knew that it was madness to blame an innocent baby for the outcome of her life, but she was not a rational person. It had been apparent since the moment of this little boy's birth, that he would suffer rejection at the hands and heart of his mother. She was very cold, while withholding love and affection from him.

It is natural for parents and children to love one another unconditionally. Babies are born totally dependent upon their parents. They are helpless and can only survive with love and nurturing from the parents. Parents need to feed, clean, and meet every need. When past the season of total dependence, a child learns who they can count on. A relationship develops that sets the stage for all other relationships in the life of each child. If that trust is broken for any reason, young lives can be altered for a life time. Children who miss receiving unconditional love at the beginning often have trouble trusting people later in life and they are set on a constant life long quest to find the love they did not receive from their parents.

That describes the life of John Chrisagis. His mother's rejection of him set him on a quest to get his mother's approval. He strove to be obedient, listened and obeyed every rule. He worked hard around the house to please her. Oftentimes, he bent over backwards striving to be kind.

As he walked home from school one day, John saw the most beautiful wild flowers at the edge of the woods. To the stunning purple and white flower, he gazed and just knew his mother would love them. It was not a special occasion, but he picked them ever so tenderly creating a beautiful bouquet intended to be a blessing for his mother. As he walked home clutching this natural treasure in his small hands, he imagined his mother's pleasure in the beautiful gift. He imagined how wonderful it would be and that this act of kindness would win her affection. He rushed home with great excitement. He ran onto the porch and swung the screen door open and happily yelled out, "Mom, Mommy." Helena answered from the bedroom rather bothered, "What do you want?" John held out the bouquet and with a big smile said, "Here Mommy. I love you."

John's mother took the bouquet from him and silently stared at them for a few minutes. She then responded, "What is this?" she snapped at little John. "These are weeds, what is wrong with you? Why would you bring weeds into this house?" She stormed away in anger to the front door. John's countenance changed as his mother spilled her anger all over him. Like water the her hate and anger poured all over John from head to toe. He stood in stunned silence wondering what he did wrong. He wondered why he was always so wrong. He did not look at her rejection as a character flaw of his mother, in his young mind he thought that he was the problem. Her words cut like a knife and made him feel invisible. He stood there not knowing what to do; he really wished he were invisible at that moment. Vanishing into the air would have made it all be better. His mother tossed the flowers out the door, walked coldly past John and went back to her household chores.

John stood silently with a broken heart, staring at his beautiful flowers. Even as a small child he realized that he would never measure up in his mother's eyes. He thought about how different her responses to him were than to his younger brother, Spiro. She was harsh with him, but little Spiro was the apple of her eye. Spiro could do no wrong and even if he did the responsibility always landed on John's shoulders. It wasn't Spiro's fault, nor Demitrius's fault… It was all the doing of one tormented woman, and that woman was Helena herself. The whole situation was way beyond sad. She took an innocent frail life and purposefully tried to destroy him, making that little one responsible for the failings of an adult who should have known better… an adult who should have been fully responsible for the problems she created rather than blame a small child. Unfortunately, the consequences of sin do have a ripple effect that can reach far beyond the sinner's life. For a mother to take the little gift that God had placed in her arms and refuse to hold it tenderly in loving care is an abomination to God and the child. It was a sad situation.

Chapter 15

Lacey's Revelation

Much time had passed since Nick and Lacey attended the *Legends Concert*, but that night everything in their lives and relationship changed. Since that night, their obsessions with the DeFilippos and their growing family kept them occupied. The more they learned the more intrigued they became.

Pictured above: The Chrisagis Brothers publicity photo for their Award Winning CD and Best Duo Award of 2016.

At this point, they spent most of their time together sharing stories of this precious family. As they compared notes and shared stories, they figured out a game plan for learning more. It seemed the more they learned the more stories remained to be heard. This family not only lived a rich fulfilling life themselves, they were of a mind and heart to do the same for all those around them. The DeFilippos' lives were richer than most. It was not a wealth built with a big bank account or large financial investments, but a wealth of lives intertwined with love and compassion. These people were far richer than the wealthiest man in the world. One evening as they examined their notes they came up with a great idea.

Since learning that Marguerite had been very ill as a child, they thought looking into the medical records of the family would prove insightful. Lacey was in a perfect position at the hospital to access that type of information. It would take time to find such old records but the wealth of information they could glean would prove invaluable. They may even find the information that would help solve the puzzle of the two dates on the tombstone. This little idea renewed their energy and excitement to continue learning more.

Nick suggested, "It is true that we know Margie was a sick child but why not look into the records of Carmella and Anthony, too. We could learn so much."

Lacey agreed, "I will put that request in tomorrow but remember this will take a great deal of time."

Nick responded, "That is fine, we have time. But something is bugging me… What were the names of the Brothers who hosted the *Legends Concert* we attended?"

Lacey quickly responded, "The Chrisagis Brothers! Wait a minute, John Chrisagis?! Could the famous Chrisagis Brothers be the children of John and Marguerite?"

"Exactly, and great deduction. That's what I thought. You know Lacey, it is no coincidence that I stumbled from the concert with the Chrisagis Brothers to the graveyard with Anthony DeFilippo who may be their grandfather. It's as if Anthony or Carmella are possessing me and leading me to this entire family, so I can tell their story." Nick pondered in wonderment.

Lacey agreed but added, "I agree with what you are saying, but I think it is the Holy Spirit leading you on this journey of discovery, not one of the DeFilippo's." Nick got a bit uncomfortable and said, "Lacey, let's not go there with that spiritual stuff and God hocus pocus."

Lacey laughed saying, "You went there Nick. Haha! I guess it is easier for you to believe that a dead man or dead woman is leading you or possessing your body, then having God guide you. Now that is funny."

Nick got frustrated and replied, "I guess… but this entire thing has me spooked. I haven't been able to sleep and it's now consuming me to know more." "Why don't you just contact the Chrisagis

Brothers Ministries and see if they can possibly tell you the entire story, if they are related in any way to these people whose lives we are looking into," Lacey asked. "That would be easy but to get through to them and their agents may take weeks... I want to know now. Besides, I want to let whatever or whoever is leading my body, thoughts and path to continue because I think they have a lot to teach me.... I don't want something quick. That may sound dumb, I want to turn over every stone to find truth. I don't want the Brothers to paint my thoughts one way or the other... I like how this person or thing is guiding me to each family member and secrets," Nick amazingly said.

When they were finished discussing the logistics of their search for information, they sat quietly for a few minutes when Lacey finally broke the silence. "With all we are learning about the DeFilippo and now the Chrisagis families the one thing that stands out to me is their strength and their faith."

Nick replied, "I agree, faith is a big part of their lives and their strength is what creates a great legend." Lacey went on, "Well, the DeFilippo's surely knew more than their fair share of struggles." Nick answered, "That is true." She continued with concern in her voice, "I wonder if my faith would be as strong as theirs if I were subject to all the struggles they went through." She went on, "I just know that my faith has not been tested. I guess I'm really blessed in some respects, free of much trouble." Nick responded, "You are lucky."

She asked, "I can't help but wonder if I have been truly blessed. It seems to me that struggles can either cause faith to grow deeper or to die altogether." She questioned, "I wonder if during hardship, would I cling to God or walk away?"

She went on to share her story, "Faith is something I grew up with and as I grew I accepted everything my parents taught me. Faith was a part of life and that is how it has been. I just wonder if I had to face what the DeFilippo's struggled through would my faith stay as strong as theirs or would it crumble under stress and strain."

Without being a man of faith Nick had no clue of how to respond but he added, to be supportive, "You would be fine, you are strong." With that answer, Lacey felt smacked in the face with their spiritual differences. She wondered if this relationship was what she really wanted. She always dreamed of a husband who shared her faith. Nick seemed to be a great match for her. They were compatible in work and play. They enjoyed a lot of the same pastimes. They were a great match but the one thing that they differed on was very important. For the first time now, the magnitude of this difference became quite clear to Lacey. Silently, she sat wondering if her faith would survive this season of miracles. After all, if there are no problems there is no need for miracles.

Chapter 16

A Budding Romance

After knowing each other for five years, it could be said that John wore Margie down and, in that a relationship grew. In the five years of knowing one another, she learned that he would be an honorable man to her. Margie had to see this before she would consider being serious about Johnny (as she called him), because his reputation preceded him.

John fell in love with her family. Anthony was always very kind to him but a little standoffish. Carmella instantly treated him as if he were a son. In fact, Carmella was the loving, sweet, devoted mother he always longed for. John fell in love not only with Margie, but he fell in love with her family. Margie's parents filled a void in his life and John loved the cooking; her mother cooked wonderful meals.

During the times of fellowship with her family is when he learned how to be a good man. He so benefitted from the relationship with the DeFilippo's. In them he found companionship, acceptance, and the love he longed for his entire life. This simple relationship between a boy and a girl grew to be a family

Pictured above:
John Chrisagis
and Marguerite DeFilippo
fall in love and get engaged.

relationship. Perhaps out of his loneliness he found a way to make a lasting relationship. A relationship developed between him and Margie leading toward marriage. Margie knew this was not the time to let her guard down. She refused to give up the standards, which she set for herself. Any time he tried to touch her leg or get cuddly would only prompt her to smack him.

After five years of seeing one another, Marguerite made a move, which no one expected. The prim and proper Margie was tired of waiting for a marriage proposal. After all it was time to get on with things if their lives were meant to progress. John seemed to be dragging his feet so Margie came up with a plan.

She called John and made a date to cook dinner for him at her house. Just before the chosen evening was at hand Margie and her mother prepared a feast for him. Everything was perfect. The table linens were crisply pressed without wrinkles or creases. Margie placed candles in the middle of the table. The aroma of the lovingly prepared food filled the house. When John arrived, he showed up with flowers that were the perfect addition to the beautiful table. They sat down to eat and talk. Before their evening was done, Marguerite had something very important to discuss with John. She started the conversation by telling him that she loved him. She explained that they had been in their relationship for five years and with her health issues she was not guaranteed a long life. She went on to explain that she had things to do no matter how much time God would give her. Marriage and having children were on the top of her list. That night she gave him an ultimatum and calmly explained he had a choice. He would either marry her or leave her alone. She refused to waste any more time waiting on him.

Margie gave John a lot to think about since that evening. His head was spinning with the decision that lay before him. He was unable to sleep. Just before dawn the next morning, he made his decision. He knew that he needed to make a commitment because the thought of losing her was too much to bear. She meant so much to him that he just knew what he had to do. A few days following their dinner, John met with Anthony and Carmella to let them know his intent to marry their daughter. This turned out to be a difficult conversation for him. Her parents were very apprehensive to give him their blessing. Since having Rheumatic Fever as a small child, Margie suffered with a heart condition. This result made her tire easily with weakness. Her parents were concerned that if she married and became pregnant that her body might not be able to handle the stress of a pregnancy. Their concern was not for John who wanted to marry their daughter. Both Anthony and Carmella sensed he was hard working and that their daughter's needs would be met. They knew John well, liked him and they all got along. Margie's health and well being was their main concern. They asked that John give them a little time to think and pray about this request. John agreed to abide by their wishes.

In the meantime, Margie made her desires known to her parents. She had not begged her parents for anything else with as much enthusiasm. After much deliberation and prayer, Anthony and Carmella realized a valuable lesson of faith learned through their daughter. Since Margie had been sick, they had treated her like a fragile egg, one who required much attention and care through life.

Yes, the parents' biggest job is to protect their children from harm and that is so easy to do when they are little. In the love of their nest all the bad guys were kept outside. The diligence of a good parent who keeps a watchful eye on their child is a gift. As the child grows, they loosen the reigns but are still there to help them figure out how to handle any situation that arises. The years pass, and parents learn that they sadly are no longer able to protect their child from a broken world or catch every raindrop that falls. They know that their child needs to have the freedom to make decisions, make mistakes, suffer from them and grow. Perhaps one of the hardest lessons for a parent is that they cannot save their child from the human condition. No matter how hard, a parent needs to let go and give their child the freedom to live their own life. Many believe that the birth of a child is the most painful part of parenting but, the most painful part of parenting is the slow, steady process of letting go. The love between a parent and a child is the closest example of love to that of God and His people. God loves all people and He looks on each one, seeing the uniqueness for which they were created. It is theirs alone. He stamps them in His image, with great joy and care. He pours all that He is into all they are. Like a parent, He marvels at His creation as the best thing He has ever done.

But what He does next is amazing and shows the true depth of His love for us. After He invests all the effort to make each person uniquely in His own image He does something more incredible. He gives them free will. His love is so great that He gives them the decision to love or not love Him. The Creator does not force the created to worship, adore and love Him… Instead, He gives the created a choice. Just like a parent, He gives His child the freedom to grow away from Him. Think of the pain when those He created reject Him. They walk away as if nothing is lost or no relationship is broken.

As parents, it can feel like total rejection when a child starts moving away from them as they grow. It is not that they do not love their parents, but in order to become a healthy, productive adult they do need to grow and sometimes move away. It is a natural normal process that feels anything but natural or normal. As they grow, you let go of being their whole world. Their world expands to include more people, so you let go of time that used to be only for you. They leave to prepare for their life's work, the parents then have to let go as their child leaves home. They meet the one they have been waiting a life time to find so you let go as they build a whole new life away from you. It is not that the child will not love you, but it will be different.

Anthony and Carmella did not really want to let go enough for Marguerite to marry but after much prayer they felt it was right. No matter her health concerns, and their concerns for her life they knew they had to let her live her life. They realized that she was ultimately in God's hands and that He knew the beginning of her days till the end of them. They had to let go to let her grow to the next stage of their lives as a family. So, Marguerite DeFilippo married John Chrisagis and the next chapter of this family's life was about to unfold.

Chapter 17

Mr. and Mrs. John Chrisagis

On June 6,1964, John and Marguerite tied the knot in a beautiful wedding. Neighbor and friend, Michele Vinci hailed it as "The most beautiful wedding of that era. John and Margie were the most gorgeous couple I have ever seen."

Cousin Gae said, "Margie was the most beautiful bride and ran rings around Jackie Kennedy."

The photographer for the wedding Jay Stock said, "Marguerite defined perfect beauty. She put me on the map as a photographer with the wedding photos." In fact, those photos of Marguerite won him first place as Photographer of the Year.

Cousin Frank Savarese, who was part of the wedding party added, "It was a huge honor to be a part of the wedding. I will forever remember that beautiful day and how happy the family will be to have a guy like John in it. He instantly became my best friend."

Pictured above: This photo of Marguerite won an award for Photographer Jay Stock as Most Beautiful Bride and photo of that year June 6, 1964.

As can be seen from all those who spoke about that glorious day it was beautiful, but not perfect because of the problems that Margie encountered upon marrying John Chrisagis.

Marguerite looked like a gorgeous princess right out of a fairy tale. But this was not a fairy tale. Margie and her mother-in-law were like Snow White and the Wicked Queen (Queen Grimhilde). John's mother Helena felt great contempt for Margie because she made

John very happy and he felt true love for the very first time. Helena knew of the DeFilippo family because everyone knew everyone in the close-knit town. Helena saw Carmella and Anthony as everything she lacked. They were a happy family, something that escaped Helena. The DeFilippos enjoyed a good reputation in all areas of life, something totally foreign to Helena. She went to the wedding feeling lesser than the bride's side of the family, not really understanding why they welcomed John as part of their family. Because she felt so out of place, she started trouble for the bride and groom. It honestly was not anything out of the ordinary for John. She went up to the couple in attempts to congratulate them, but her contempt for John spilled out in her celebration of this marriage.

Helena walked up to the young couple and began insulting them. She said she could not believe that her son L.A. found anyone to marry him. L.A. was a nickname given to him since he was a young boy. L.A. stood for Lazy Ass. Marguerite stood beside John quietly listening to how his mother spoke

Pictured above:
June 6, 1964 John and Marguerite become Mr. and Mrs. John Chrisagis. They made a gorgeous couple who looked as if they were Hollywood Royalty.

to him and saw how John nervously responded to his mother. Marguerite politely and patiently responded to Helena's insults. Her response let Helena know what she refused to tolerate. Marguerite said, "Now you know John does not have a lazy bone in his body. He is the hardest worker I have ever seen. With all due respect, you will not speak ill of my husband again. I love him, he is a good man, he is filled with integrity and I plan to have children with him. So, your disrespect for him is not acceptable now or ever. Do I make myself clear?" So, with that little speech Helena knew where she stood and what was expected.

When the bridal dance began, Helena was one of the first in line to dance with Margie. As they began, Helena told her something shocking. "Margie, don't be too good to Johnny, for he doesn't deserve it. Cheat on him with other men the way I do with Demitrius. This keeps the marriage fresh."

Margie stopped the dance immediately and said, "This dance is done. As a lady, I will not give that a response. Now leave or I will forget I am a lady and throw you out myself!" Helena was thrown back by Marguerite's strength. She walked away quickly, and Margie shook inside. She was not used to fighting anyone but even a proper lady of class can be pushed. Then Demitrius Chrisagis walked over to Margie and put his strong arm around her and said, "Way to go Tiger, I feel like applauding you. No one stands up to Helena. I haven't seen an exit like that since Dorothy threw a bucket of water on the witch. You will make a good wife for John. I am looking forward to the fireworks and I will toast to that."

Margie was speechless as she stood in shock. At that moment she realized her father-in-law was not her enemy but he felt her pain and knew Helena's wicked tendencies very well. It is a smart bride who sets her boundaries when they need to be set. Margie started her married life on the right foot. She let her mother-in-law know how she wanted her husband treated and the fact that she would not tolerate anything less than respect. At that moment, in those little speeches, she took charge of her home and family.

It was short time following marriage when Margie began to ask John for a child. Since she was a little girl, she knew that all she wanted in life was to be a mother. One night she set the dinner table with baby booties as the centerpiece, to discuss the possibility of being parents. John remembered the conversation he had with his father-in-law when he asked for Margie's hand. John told her about that meeting. "I remember that afternoon as clearly as if it were yesterday. I was so nervous. I know your parents liked me but still sometimes your father seemed less than eager for our relationship to progress. As I sat in the living room with your mother and father, I told them that I loved you and intended to marry you. I let them know that I could provide for you and I intended to take care of you for the rest of my life."

Margie listened carefully as John continued. "Well, they reassured me that they felt as if I would be a good husband for you. Your parents went on to explain that your health was their biggest concern. As often happens after marriage, children come along, and they were concerned that a pregnancy would harm your health. They explained the disease that caused your heart issues. They asked that we not have children to protect your health. I would like to respect their wishes."

Margie remained quiet as he spoke. It took her a few moments to collect her thoughts and respond to his concerns. "Johnny you need to know I have had two dreams since I was a little girl. My first dream was to be a wife. Marrying you made my first dream come true, and that makes me so happy. Being married to you gives me someone to care for and to live for. My parents and you are my family now. The second dream I had was to be a mother. I have imagined feeling a little life growing inside of me. To feel the first little breath of life; I can imagine it feeling like butterflies in my belly. I have dreamed of holding my child, smelling that beautiful new baby smell. I would treasure the joy of being up at night with the little one as the rest of the world sleeps. I would sit at our big picture window rocking our baby. In the stillness of night, I would stare out the window into the night realizing just how small I am in the big world. I would hold the child close to my chest listening to its quiet rhythmic breathing. In that moment I would realize how big God is, and feel rather small but miraculously cared for and loved by God. I want to feel that peace and share it with the child I love. My dream is to give all that I have to a child, my child.

I have prayed for my children since I was a teenager. I have been praying for their well-being, praying for their health, praying that God would bless me with them in His perfect time. I have also prayed that my health issues would not be a problem. I want to be a mother. Can't we pray and ask God to protect me if He chooses to bless us with a child? We have trusted Him with other aspects of our lives, can't we trust Him for this?" John listened intently as his wife spoke from her heart.

She ended her request by sharing with John, "I know you are concerned for my health and pregnancy. Why don't we approach it this way? Let's put the decision of children into God's hands. Let's pray that if my body can handle pregnancy and birth that He would bless us with a baby. And, if God doesn't bless us with children for whatever reason we will accept His decision. I will accept His will, but I cannot believe that God would put this desire in my heart without fulfilling it."

It was a solution that both John and Margie could support. They left their decision to have a family in the very capable hands of their God.

They spent their first year of marriage learning who they were as a couple. About a year into the marriage they were blessed with the news that they were expecting a baby. Her doctors took extra care with the pregnancy. They conducted extensive tests to make sure that Margie and the baby were okay. For Anthony and Carmella this time was marked more with prayer and cautious optimism. Even John had his unspoken concerns, but things were set in course and there was no turning back. Much to the surprise of

Pictured above: Marguerite has her biggest dream come true when she has a healthy son that she named Anthony John Chrisagis.

the DeFilippos, her doctors, and even John, this pregnancy was picture perfect. The happy couple was blessed with a perfect baby boy whom they named Anthony John Chrisagis, named after Margie's father and her husband John. God gave Margie her heart's desire and she felt as if she were over the moon. She did all the things of which she had dreamed. Late at night she silently rocked her baby in front of the picture window, cuddling her child and thanking her Lord. Against all odds, He had made her dream come true. With her hands in His she could do anything He had for her to do. They were a happy little family thrilled with the little miracle sent by God.

Anthony and Carmella DeFilippo were thrilled, and like all new grandparents they wondered at the miracle for which they had been blessed. Becoming a grandparent is always exciting. New parents stand at the beginning of their journey of parenthood with vague ideas of how life will be. Grandparents stand at the end of physical parenting with all the knowledge of years of experience. They stand with an empty nest, the job of parenting a memory, so they bring practical experience to their new role. With open arms and hearts, they long to love a child again. That little one, fresh from the heart of God, is placed right in the void left in their hearts and in their empty nest. With the arrival of a grandchild there is a wonder that returns in the home.

Little Anthony Chrisagis became the new light in the lives of the DeFilippo family. After all the health struggles with Margie they were blessed with this perfect outcome. The sleepless nights of prayer and worry were all worth it. This was one of the happiest times of their lives.

Now the Chrisagis' experience as grandparents vastly differed from the DeFilippo's. Demitrius Chrisagis was a man's man without much interest in babies. Helena's response to the birth of little Anthony was very different than anyone would have expected. First, she made it quite clear that she disliked the name Anthony. In fact, she was bold enough to tell Margie and John how displeased she was with their choice of names. This was strange since Helena's behavior had always been less than normal. When they were alone the young parents discussed Helena's behavior. From what they thought, John's mother was upset because they named him Anthony, for her father. From the beginning, John knew his mother felt inferior to Margie's parents. They reasoned that she felt as if this was another way that her parents were favored over his. Years passed before they learned the real reason for her disdain.

Chapter 18

Blessed with Twins

Time moves on, marching into change and growth. After the wedding of John and Margie, life for both the DeFilippos and Chrisagis families moved into a new season. Out of concern for her lovely daughter Margie, Carmella had Anthony build an extra apartment onto their house above the grocery store. There, she could keep an eye on Margie's health with the beautiful new baby Anthony John. Beautifully decorated, the small apartment looked like a doll house with lots of love. You could feel God in each room.

Margie and John were the happiest couple anyone would ever find. They filmed every part of little Anthony John's life from his earliest movements, to his first words, and first steps. The walls and photo albums were filled with this beautiful little boy. Anthony John was a baby who should have been in the movies. He had thick curly black hair with long side-burns. He had the roundest dark brown eyes that lit up and danced when he saw his mother. Anthony John also had a perfect smile that beamed from ear-to-ear with cuteness and personality. Margie took time journaling each day in a book because she adored her precious son and felt as if she could not get enough of him. He knew he was loved, and he also knew he had both his parents wrapped around his cute little fingers.

Pictured above: Anthony John Chrisagis looked so sweet, like a little model.

As time went on Anthony John grew and Margie grew weaker. Because of the strain of the pregnancy with little Anthony John, her heart

Pictured above:
The twins (Brian and Shawn) arrive on March 16, 1968 born with life-threatening allergies, with a short life expectancy.

walls were beyond reviving and the muscles weakened beyond the point of repair. Three years had passed, and Margie was expectant with child again. When doctors learned about her pregnancy, they advised against carrying the pregnancy to term because of what it might do to her health. Neither she nor John would have entertained the idea of abortion since they were Catholic. Margie grew up an only child. She never wanted to subject her child to the loneliness she felt as she grew. She needed to give little Anthony a sibling.

Getting pregnant was easy but carrying a baby to term proved difficult for Margie each time. This second pregnancy proved to be just that. As things progressed, she became deathly ill. Things were so hard through this pregnancy that Carmella shut the store down to devote her time to the care of Margie and little Anthony, while John worked. The entire family worked together to see this pregnancy come to a healthy conclusion. Margie weighed only 98 pounds, so when she got pregnant, she got pregnant all over. She got so big that she looked like Madame De La Grande Bouche from the movie Beauty and The Beast with skinny arms, legs and the face of an angel. Margie's parents were scared she was going to "pop" because she was so fragile, dainty and thin to be carrying such a large baby. Her legs could barely hold all the additional weight that she had to carry.

One-night John and Margie lay in bed watching Margie's belly move up and down as the baby moved in her womb. It is amazing to be at the part of the pregnancy when the evidence of movement clearly shows that there is a baby inside. Each of them were thrilled to see the imprint of little hands and feet. The baby kicked so hard that it seemed as if the child would force its way out through the mother's belly. While the young couple enjoyed this simple pleasure, they noticed that something seemed very strange. The baby, or so they thought, pressed on the abdominal wall so that they could clearly see prints of hands and feet. As they each marveled at every single body part identifiable, in a moment, they counted four foot prints on Margie's belly! How could this be, and they surely would not have believed this if they had not witnessed it together. They knew human babies only had two feet, so they were curious and expecting the doctor to tell them more. The doctor confirmed they were having twins! He explained the reason for not knowing about twins inside was due to weak heart rates. Now the doctor and his staff really pressed for an abortion because they thought Margie would never be able to carry these twins full-term and if she did, it most likely would kill her and the twins. Margie refused to have an abortion. However, John wanted his wife healthy and alive, so he pondered the thought of abortion. Yet, Margie won. With her faith in God, she continued to carry the twins through prayers.

Some years before, Marguerite had a dream that she had three sons. Since that dream, she had prayed for the three boys that she knew God planned to give her. Every day the pregnancy got harder and harder. The whole family did their part to take care of Margie and the twins she carried. The extra work and effort were all bathed in prayer. This family valued life and did everything necessary in order to protect it.

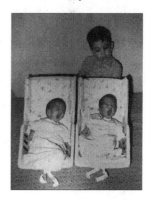

The twins were born three months early in North Wheeling Hospital in West Virginia on March 16, 1968 aided by Doctor Herman Rubin. Margie and John named them Brian Zachary Chrisagis, who was born first, and Shawn Michael Chrisagis born two minutes later. They

Pictured above: Anthony taking his job as older brother seriously with Brian and Shawn.

were small. Shawn weighed in at 2 pounds and Brian at 2 and a half pounds. Margie was weak as this pregnancy took so much from her already-strained body. Instinctly, Margie wanted to protect her offspring. Having come through a traumatic pregnancy only made her more protective of her twins. Margie had two who needed special care, so she focused on her newborn sons. They needed her since they were very sick.

Brian and Shawn were seriously premature. They had even more serious issues. Their color resembled a purplish green color and their little bodies were covered in lumps. The doctors, John, and Margie all knew something was seriously wrong. Little Brian and Shawn were put through a battery of tests. While all this was going on, time passed and yet the boys failed to grow. After many tests, doctors determined that these two sickly babies suffered from a very rare condition found in one out of every fifty thousand live births, and more prevalent in males. The boys' immune systems were very weak, so they were kept in the hospital. They suffered from SCID or Severe Combined Immune Deficiency, a condition caused by the mutation of various genes. Infants with this condition suffer through many bacterial, viral, and fungal infections. Their weakened immune systems made them susceptible to everything and they had to be protected against germs and dirt. Both of them also suffered with severe allergies to everything. They were allergic to the sun, almost every food, grass, every kind of fabric and materials, plus indoor lighting. The only foods the boys could eat were rice cakes, soybean milk, sardines, and peanut butter.

The strain of the rare condition seemed impossible for the family to handle. John and Margie traveled back and forth to the hospital to visit the babies in incubators for the first two years of their lives. Brian and Shawn weren't growing the way the doctors hoped, and in those first two years they received non-stop testing. The twins were at the hospital more than they were home. Scary times were felt by all the family. Margie's parents took care of little Anthony, while John worked five jobs to pay for all the medical bills while Margie stayed at the hospital with the boys the entire time. After work, John traveled daily on very little sleep back and forth to the hospital to support his wife and see his ill sons.

Margie never left the twins' side. She even stayed in the middle of both incubators holding both of their tiny hands. She refused to let them go through this alone. As the exhaustion and tension increased, so the medical bills rose, too. At one point, the bill amounted to four hundred thousand dollars. This was all new for these young parents. Life seemed simpler when little Anthony was born. Margie's health was the only one in question. For her that was much easier to deal with than her experience with the twins. She would have taken all their suffering onto herself if she could have. With the twins, her experience was quite different. Her health issues were still prevalent in every decision that needed to be made. But even before their birth it became quite clear that were serious health issues existed for these babies. This made everything much harder for Margie. She almost felt responsible for their condition, reasoning that if her health had been better, then the babies' health would have been, too. It was at this time that Margie really lived out a motto which she had held fast to her whole life. Her special acrostic is for the word "FAMILY".

F-Forget

A-About

M- Me

I-I

L-Love

Y-You

Pictured at right: Marguerite's heart continues to worsen, but she does not want to miss a moment with her boys. Here she is with her twins. She was the best!

This sweet little acrostic summarizes how Margie Chrisagis lived for the people who God had blessed her with. Margie's health and special needs for twin boys created a very hard time for the whole family, one that lasted for years. These boys needed continual care, special diets, and protection away from the sun. After many tests, the determined outcome resulted in nothing more that could be done for these little boys. Sadly, the doctors sent them home to die. During this time, Margie's dearest first cousin and godmother (Aurora's daughter), MaryJane, gave her a book called, They Will Live and Not Die by Lester Sumrall. MaryJane, a born-again Christian, prayed often with Margie. The book encouraged Margie to take an active role in believing God for healing, needs to be met, and other steps of faith by giving her the scriptures of God's promises for His people. She did more than just read it, she digested it. It became life to her and she used it as a guideline of how to pray for her babies. This book became a treasure of information and support as she stood in faith. With her spiritual muscles flexed and ready for battle, she took charge to see that her sons were spared, healed, and used by God.

As they brought the twins home, the house needed remodeling to accommodate the boys' needs. Of all the allergies they had, the strangest one was the sun. They could not be in the sun at all. Even the sun coming through the windows proved problematic for these babies. So, life needed to be altered and accommodated for the twins. For years, their illness dictated all they did. Even with an altered life, they made it work. The family adapted very well as life progressed. As all three boys grew, little Anthony became the boy's best friend and the light of their world. The babies developed skin conditions that needed treatment every hour, with creams and bandages.

Little Anthony made a very good big brother for the twins. He became like a little daddy to them running around to make sure they were always okay. He was old enough to know that something was wrong with them, so he needed to take extra care. As a good big brother, he wanted to protect the babies he loved. Margie noticed that he acted more like a daddy than a brother. This would not do, so Margie tried to make him play with the twins. Anthony needed to realize that he was a brother, just three years older than them and not responsible for everything that went on in their lives. She wanted to make sure he remained a happy child and not carry the family's problems on his little shoulders. She knew that little Anthony needed to be a child and enjoy the relationship of being brothers, growing up together.

Margie's father Anthony stepped in to be little Anthony's playmate. He took Anthony out to the park, the zoo, the Ice Capades, or to play ball outside so he would have a normal childhood. Anthony had lots of fun with his Pap. When Johnny was around, he did the same, but John had his hands full with five jobs, paying bills, staying up through the night with the boys. He tried to give Margie some rest with her bad heart, and strived to be the perfect dad and husband while keeping peace between his mother Helena and all her destructive schemes. Little Anthony became obsessed with the TV series "Batman" starring Adam West. He always watched the show dressed in a Batman costume sitting with his dad, John.

Little Anthony wanted everything of Batman and dreamed of being Batman fighting crime and protecting his family from evil doers. After work one day John brought home an action figure of Superman for Anthony to play with, thinking that he would enjoy a new super hero. Anthony loved the action hero but he then laid it on a shelf. He continued to play with his Batman action figures.

John was puzzled, so he questioned Anthony, "Son, why don't you like Superman? He is even a better super hero than Batman is… he is stronger, faster, and can do anything. Give him a chance."

Anthony responded, "Dad, I'm Batman. I could never be Superman. I'm not worthy. Superman is you! You are my superman, because you are the greatest hero of all to me!"

This touched John's heart. He worked all his life to be loved and that day his son made him feel as if he were the richest man on earth. He felt the love he always longed for being a dad.

The seasons changed and months rolled along, one after another, if it weren't for Margie's sweet parents, the young couple could never have made it through those trying years. Margie and the twins needed much care as each season of life took place. The twins were very active babies. Shawn was the first to "goo" at three months and the first to say "Mama" and the first to say "DaDa" at seven months. Both Margie and Johnny were thrilled to hear Shawn call for them so early; they leaped for joy. Shawn crawled at five months. He started talking up a storm and at eleven months said "baby" and touched Brian. He then said "ba" meaning bottle and "Ah" to call Anthony and "Na" to call Nana.

Anthony excitedly ran every time Shawn called for him. It was a big deal for a small child and made him feel important. But Brian was the first to receive a tooth and the first to walk at seven months. The family was thrilled to see him being the first at something too. They were very concerned that something may have been wrong because Shawn appeared to be the more aggressive child and learned more quickly. Brian's first words were "Nana and Pap", which brought such joy to Margie's parents.

In December 1968, Brian became deathly ill with a 102 degree fever for three days. Margie and Carmie stayed awake with him all day and night soaking him in alcohol and laying him on ice water. Margie cried so hard because she feared that he would go into convulsions or that the fever might harm his brain. Nana was amazing through this as she used an old Italian method to bring down the fever. Antibiotics, aspirins, and alcohol rubs were applied around the clock. Mommy and Nana cuddled and cried for Brian around the clock.

At eleven months, Brian's finger got caught in the bathroom door as little Anthony shut the door. The finger was completely severed. Everyone in the house heard crying and they didn't know which child needed help. They first thought it was Shawn since he made the most noise holding his finger, but it turned out to be Brian.

As his twin, Shawn felt Brian's pain. Nana hurried and put Brian's finger that had fallen to the floor in ice while Margie grabbed Brian and held him tight. Aunt Francie and Gae were there; they grabbed Shawn and Anthony to comfort them both. Anthony really had a hard time with this because he so carefully cared for and protected his little baby brothers.

So Aunt Francie and Gae stayed with Anthony and Shawn. Johnny got the car and rushed Brian, Margie, Nana and Pap to the family doctor, who was Dr. Schlitzauers, to see what could be done with the finger. Schlitzauer sent them to the hospital to see Dr. Carson. He was able to sew the finger on.

They wrapped Brian in a blanket, but they couldn't numb the finger or put him to sleep because of his allergies. So, Brian suffered terrible pain and the doctors had to strap him down. It took the doctor two hours to have the finger re-attached in the Emergency Room. This broke the family's hearts and Margie blamed herself for not being there to keep him from harm. Then the doctors made Margie lie down with smelling salts. She stayed with Brian the entire time at the hospital. One week later Margie was taken to the Emergency Room for her nerves. Since Brian's accident, she suffered from neural tension and had an emotional break-down; the family was concerned that she might have a heart attack.

A home filled with small children is a busy place. Every day Marguerite and Nana Carmella would put salve on the twins' skin to keep their skin from breaking out. Cousins MaryJane and her four sisters (which were Aurora's five daughters) all searched for a cure for Brian and Shawn. The sisters shipped materials and fabrics for the boys from all over the world, so that Margie and Carmie could make them clothes to wear without causing an allergic reaction. Carmella's early years of being a seamstress with her mother, Angela, became invaluable to the family. Aurora's daughters also shipped boxes of vitamins and soybean products to help the boys get the nutrition they needed. All the family members kept the boys alive when the doctors gave them a death sentence. Brian and Shawn were back and forth to the hospital almost weekly for treatments needed to survive.

When Margie took the boys to the hospital, whether with John or her mom Carmie, they had to totally cover them up to protect them from the environment around them. Then the doctors and nurses would lay the boys down on their medical tables and put needles all over Brian and Shawn's backs to feed them nutrients, and whatever else they needed to stay alive. Margie and Johnny (or Carmella) would hold the twins' hands through the entire procedure.

Anthony stayed home with his Pap. One day Anthony felt scared because he saw Pap smoking. He heard Nana always say to Pap that smoking could kill him and those who take in second hand smoke. So with that on his mind, when Pap fell asleep Anthony took the cigarettes, ate some of them and the rest he hid in the oven. When Nana turned on the oven, she smelled cigarette smoke and the oven looked as if it were on fire. She found Anthony green as could be throwing up everywhere. Needless to say, it was another emotional moment for Margie, Nana, John and Pap.

With children running in different directions, speeds and schedules there is an effort on the part of smart parents to deplete energy in whatever way they can curb the boundless energy. Many young families spend countless hours in the park or in their yards. The Chrisagis family had a very different lifestyle. Their fun and activities were indoors, unlike those of other families.

Mother tried to keep them busy and entertained. She noticed that these boys had their own language, which the family jokingly referred to as their "twin talk". She quickly noticed they had a natural creative aptitude for drawing and working off one another. She saw how all of her children had their own amazing personalities. All were their own person. Anthony was extremely smart, with a wild imagination and with a love for music. He started organ lessons and loved singing. He was a ham who loved attention and was so cute that attention from others came easily. He wrote his own plays and had his brothers act it out with him. Brian was the clown who could entertain for hours. He loved making people laugh and was very dramatic in every way. Brian never knew a stranger and would just go up to anyone who visited as if he knew them forever. Brian was most like his dad John in personality traits. He loved people and craved love in return. He never liked to see anyone upset. Shawn was extremely sensitive and shy, hiding behind his mom and Nana all the time. Shawn cried easily because he always felt other people's pain. If he heard his mom or Nana cry, he was there to comfort them… his entire world turned upside down if he didn't see Mommy and Nana in the room together. Shawn was most like his mom, Margie, in personality traits. Shawn also organized Brian and Anthony even though he was the youngest of the three boys.

As she watched the boys, Margie came up with an idea. When they drew a picture, she asked them questions about the figures in the picture. She encouraged them to name the characters in the pictures and with that information she created stories to tell the boys. These stories were not only entertaining, but Mother made sure there were character lessons designed to teach the twins important values. The boys enjoyed this, and they spent hours drawing so their mother would weave wonderful stories out of their work. She taught them concepts such as self-worth, kindness, courage, manners, sharing and love. She taught them to care for others and to grow into men of strength and character. Though they were still very sick, Margie believed that they would be healed by her God.

Chapter 19

A Thorn in the Flesh

John and Margie were well-matched in their marriage. Neither of them brought drama into the marriage; that role remained exclusively for John's mother, Helena. Her drama started from the moment they said, "I do". She started trouble and continued that cycle for many years. When the babies were born, for some reason she had trouble understanding why the twins had an abnormal condition. Really, that should not have been a surprise because she questioned Margie about her own sickness. She always tried to get under her daughter-in-law's skin. Even when she appeared to be nice, many family members sensed an ulterior motive.

One day, Helena had to drive Margie to an appointment with her heart doctor. Helena took that opportunity to needle Margie. At Margie's appointment, Helena talked to the doctor and he told her how important it was for Margie not to have stress because of her weakened heart. So, Helena pondered in her heart just how harmful stress was to Margie's health and decided to be the snake in the grass. John's mother knew that he worked a great deal to pay the outstanding medical bills. She knew that he was not home much. Helena took the opportunity to plant seeds of doubt in her young daughter-in-law's mind. She tried to convince the young mother that any good-looking husband who spends too much time away from home just had to be stepping out on his wife. She also told Margie that since the three boys were born, Margie had gotten fat, sloppy, and unattractive for a man

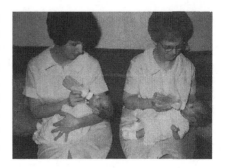

Pictured at right: The twins have two sweet mothers loving them day and night. Pictured is their Mom (Margie) and their Nana (Carmie). Margie always said the acronyms of Family was "Forget About Me I Love You". She sacrificed her entire life to love her children.

with Johnny's appetite. Margie cried and carried those unkind words on her mind and deep in her heart.

One day Gae called Margie to let her and the family know that her mother, Francie, was near death and wanted the family together at the hospital. Now Margie never let anyone watch her children except her parents, or Aunt Francie, or her cousins Gae or MaryJane, but she found herself in a predicament. John told Margie to let his mother watch over the boys, because he thought it might bring peace to his family's problems. Margie argued but then against her better judgment she had no other choice but to ask Helena to come stay with the boys.

Helena agreed to watch the boys and she took that moment to exact vengeance on John. So, she decided to open a window and put the twins in the front of it while they laid in their basinets. The night was a frigid cold blizzard night. This type of weather could easily kill anyone, especially Brian and Shawn in their frail conditions. Little Anthony witnessed his grandmother doing this and insisted that she get them away from the open window. She smacked Anthony, grabbed him by the arm and threw him into a closet and locked the door. As he cried and screamed to save his little brothers, she mocked him.

Margie and John left the hospital thankful that Aunt Francie survived her nearly fatal experience. Upon returning home, Margie walked into the house to find the twins close to death. Helena's evil decisions caused Margie to go ballistic! John screamed at his mother and threw her out as they rushed the twins to the hospital. This produced a serious setback in the health and life of the boys.

Another time, the twins needed blood transfusions; they called on family members to contribute. John, Carmella ("Nana") and Anthony ("Pap") DeFilippo contributed blood to this cause. Margie also asked Helena ("Botchie") and Demitrius ("Pa-pou") to give. As they expected she refused, but Demitrius finally gave in and donated. With Demitrius' donation, the doctor found something he never expected. It had nothing to do with Brian, Shawn or Margie.

It seemed with blood drawn on all the family members they noticed something unusual when samples of John and his father Demitrius were compared. Differences were found within the blood. The doctor revealed that there was no scientific way that John could possibly be Demitrius' biological son. Everyone thought, how peculiar! Everyone that is, except Helena.

With her secret out, Helena acted like a cornered tiger coming out fiercely while fighting with her whole family. Once all the fight drained out of her, she could do nothing but confess. John happened to be present for the confession. With the demeanor of a broken soul, she quietly confessed. She was unable to look at Demitrius or John, but she stared out the window as she spoke. She kept her hands busy cleaning the sink.

She bared her heart saying, "Demitrius just before I met you, I fell in love with a wonderful man, Anthony Moretti. He was all I ever wanted in a man and we got along very well. He was the only man whom I ever loved. He was married so when I learned about my pregnancy with his baby, he had no choice but to walk away from me and fulfill his marriage obligations. I was left alone to have this baby. Though I have to tell you, I wanted to get rid of this baby. No doubt, I tried to get rid of it, but nothing worked. He hung on with a tenacity that I hated." Demitrius and John stood silently as they digested her unraveled secret.

She continued to unburden her soul, "I was pregnant with John when I met you, Demitrius. You loved me, so this seemed a good solution for my problem. You married me and reared John as your own. I appreciated your care, but as much as I tried to love you, I could not. I was and still am very much in love with Anthony Moretti. It is a moot point because he has been dead for years. Therefore, I cannot stand John because his arrival made it necessary for me to settle for a man who I never loved, and I hated my first grandson's name because it forever reminded me of the man who I could not have, yet truly loved. I loved Anthony Moretti but ironically hate the name Anthony because it reminds me of all the lies I have lived throughout the years to keep secret."

Helena paused and thought aloud, "I know the worst part is the lack of a mother's love for John. A mother is supposed to love her children, but I saw this child as the reason for the loss of the love of my life. This hatred for John started long before he was born, and it grew throughout his life. I hate everyone who makes him happy. Marguerite, so sweet, tender, and caring, was all I ever wanted to be. I hate her for making John happy. She sees great value in him and I get so jealous. I hate her for seeing in my son what I was unable to see myself." John could not believe his ears.

From the time Anthony was a small child he always knew that something was amiss between his mother and himself. He now knew the reason. John knew Anthony Moretti very well. In fact, Mr. Moretti taught John carpentry during his teenage years. He found it hard to believe that the same man was his biological father. Now he understood why they had kindred spirits and why he felt at home with Mr. Moretti.

As John silently wondered about her earth-shattering confession, the man who he thought was his father Demitrius, silently listened to this confession and just could not stand it any longer. His blood boiled in anger as he learned this truth. When he could no longer control himself, his anger exploded on Helena. He tried to strangle her. John had to pull Demitrius off Helena before he killed her. This revelation forever altered this family. It was not a loving family at all but with this new truth Demitrius and his family embarked on a spiral of hate that kept each other broken. Separation did not occur. Instead, their unloving mission was to make each other as miserable as possible.

Chapter 20

Faith in Work Boots

From a young age, John had always loved working with his hands. He possessed a natural ability to create things with tools and repair broken things. He spent hours tinkering on his building projects. As a teen, his interests drew him to employment with Anthony Moretti. Mr. Moretti was one of the most successful builders in the area. Working for him gave John the experience that proved to be valuable for his whole life. John learned at the hands of a master craftsman. He first learned the basics and as Anthony saw his aptitude for the work, he took him by the hand and molded him into a great craftsman. The two men were kindred spirits who got along very well. Moretti enjoyed sharing the wisdom of his skill with John. John enjoyed the attention, especially with someone in his life who shared his passion. The bond that John had with Mr. Moretti brought encouragement, acceptance, and direction that his life needed at that very moment.

Pictured above: John Chrisagis, the best Dad around. He gave his sons the love he never received as a child. He worked five jobs at one time to keep his family alive and well.

The relationship with Mr. Moretti and Margie's sweet parents puts his life on the course for what it would soon become. John's in-laws (Carmella and Anthony) were the loving devoted parents he needed. Truth be told, they loved him as if he were their own. Even when he needed guidance or got into trouble, the first person he ran to was his mother-in-law. She always led him with a mother's love. From a damaged and broken little boy to a young man who slowly healed, he learned to give and succeed in an adult world.

Despite the torment during John's childhood, he chose to make the best of his life. He learned the essence of true love through his beautiful wife Marguerite and their three sons. He loved his mother (Helena) but didn't like her. He always tried to see the best in everyone. He enjoyed his time fishing with his dad, Demitrius, and loved him. John was the type of guy who loved with his entire being. He loved without conditions. He loved his brother Spiro and enjoyed building houses, laying carpet, riding speed boats, driving motorcycles, jumping out of planes, skiing, and hiking with him. The two of them did everything healthy athletic men would do together. Some of his favorite memories are the times he spent with his cousins Mickey and Nina Demopoulos, Lou and Bozena Anastas. Those were moments he treasured for a life-time.

The next chapter of his life appeared bright with promise. The train wreck of childhood slowly faded into a distant past memory. The world was alive with promise. God made all things new. His heart and eyes were filled with love for one woman, Margie, who he would die for. In his adult years, he poured himself into the little family that he and his wife created. He felt blessed to have the love of a good woman. He knew just how blessed he had been, so he never took her or his family for granted. He sacrificed to care for them.

Pictured above: Anthony with his baby brothers Shawn (at legs) and Brian (in middle). These three brothers remain a tri-chord of love for each other today.

When Brian and Shawn were sick, and the bills mounted, he took on five part time jobs to get them paid off. He also kept taking Margie to the hospital in Baltimore, Maryland for her heart problems. It didn't matter to him how far he needed to travel, his faithfulness and commitment were steadfast. He chose to get the best for his family, no matter the price.

He not only provided for his family, but he blessed others, too. He owned a few houses that were income-producing for his family. He purchased them inexpensively, fixed them up and rented them out. Many times, he did not collect rent from people who were in need, he helped homeless people and sheltered them. Johnny's life shined as an example of the Christian walk with how he loved and helped everyone he knew. Everyone called him Dad.

That is hard to understand, after all he grew up without really having the love of a dad. Yet he became the "Dad" to all. It could be said that he was Jesus with skin on. Margie, the love of his life, was his rock. He did everything and gave everything for her. In all the years of their marriage she could count on his strong and tender arms to hold her in his care. As the years passed, his love for her remained consistent and steady. In fact, at the end of their time together, even though sick, he still gave his all for Margie.

Both John and Margie developed kidney failure, and were both on dialysis. The chemo therapy Margie took to battle brain cancer caused her kidneys to fail. John was in Ohio State Hospital receiving a donated kidney when the boys let him know that Margie, who was at home in Yorkville, had taken a turn for the worse. Against all common sense and the warning of the doctors who were caring for him, he checked himself out of the hospital to be with his wife when she needed him most.

He pulled plugs from the machines at the hospital and drove two hours away with all the medical monitors and bags still attached to him. He was determined to get to his beloved Margie. By the time he got home, she was very sick and had to be taken to the hospital where she took her last breath, graduating into eternity at the young age of sixty-four with her husband, mother, children, and cousins Gae and Frank by her side.

As John and Margie's sons grew up they all became famous singers in different walks of life. Anthony, the oldest of the brothers received a scholarship to the Civic Light Opera but he turned it down to serve the Lord in ministry. He received his ordination and started Anthony Chrisagis Evangelical Ministries. John and Margie were co-founders of the Ministry and guided it all the way. His younger brothers joined him in spreading the Gospel of Christ throughout the United States. The three brothers then had their own syndicated

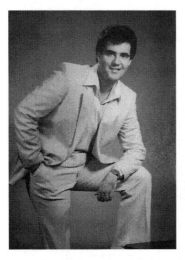

children's TV series. John created all the props, designed and made puppets along with Carmella while the brothers all performed, wrote, produced, directed and worked all the puppets. The series went on for three successful years. Margie's life ended before her sons truly stepped into their big time calling. Carmie died right after that so she saw a part of it... but John got to see it all. He was a big part of all that took place in ministering worldwide.

Pictured above:
Anthony Chrisagis
poster and CD cover

Anthony later got married and started a career as a Las Vegas entertainer, where he worked as a lounge lizard for some of Las Vegas' biggest hotels. He also traveled throughout London and released a string of LP's and CD's with his music. At the same time, Brian and Shawn became known world-wide as the Chrisagis Brothers and were seen on every Christian TV network, magazines, released tons of popular music CD's, were the first Christian music artists to appear on MTV, and produced their own Children's toyline that taught children what their parents and grandparents taught them.

Everyone loved the Chrisagis Toyline and bought the toys for their own children and grandchildren. Legendary royalty such as Jaclyn Smith, Dolly Parton and James Caviezel critically acclaimed the collection for children. The Chrisagis Brothers worked with Hollywood's biggest legends such as Erik Estrada, Jennifer O'Neill,

Jack Scalia, Lindsay Wagner and others. They performed on stage with Christian music legends such as Stephanie Boosahda (a lifelong friend), Farrell & Farrell, Scott Wesley Brown, Russ Taff, Bruce Carroll, Michael English, Sandi Patty, Phil Keaggy, John Schlitt, Jaci Velasquez, Kathy Troccoli, Evie Tornquist, Wayne Watson, Dino Kartsonakis, Reba Rambo and Dony McGuire, David Meece, Dave Boyer and others.

The Chrisagis Brothers created a traveling Legends Music Tour. They also had their own TV reality special for A&E. The Brothers had a hit radio show called It's A God Thing named after their hit song. The show featured iconic super stars such as Cheryl Ladd, Loni Anderson, Joe Penny, Kevin Sorbo and Pat Boone. The international ministry was loved by all.

The twins even won Best Duo Artists in Christian Music by the Extraordinary People Awards. Without the support of John Chrisagis, none of this would have been possible. He worked every day of his life to make his sons fulfill their God-given calling. He sacrificed everything to see that dream and vision Margie had for her sons come to pass. He did it not because he was forced, not because he was their dad but because he simply loved them so much. He was Dad every day, every second and forever.

After Margie died, John met a lovely lady named Renee' Stewart. At first his sons did not want to receive Renee' because they adored their mom so much. She was so much a part of their lives. Carmella was still alive and became the beautiful matriarch of the family at age eighty-nine. She mourned her daughter's death but wanted Johnny to live and love again.

Pictured at right:
Marguerite and John
before Margie died
of brain cancer
Christmas of 2002.

Carmie told the three sons to love Renee' because Renee' was good for their dad. Carmie "Nana" always looked out for John and her treasured grandsons. She was the epitome of love. It oozed out of every pore of her body and wherever Nana was they could feel God. She taught her grandsons to love and accept Renee'.

Then Nana died before her ninetieth birthday. So, Renee' became John's girlfriend and a precious companion whom he treated like a queen. Renee's spouse had also passed away and she often said that John showed her how a real man treats a woman. That was something she realized she had lacked with her own husband.

John later made amends with his brother Spiro who he always loved. The brothers were best friends when they were young and both could be considered "MacGyvers", because they could figure out anything and could fix anything better than anyone else. They both did everything together when they were young and when they reunited after the death of Helena years later, it was just like old times again.

Years later during John's death he saw his beautiful Margie and his father and mother-in-law waiting for him on the other side. The boys were with him in the ICU and he kept talking of the snow that appeared in the room worrying that he had not yet gotten the winter tires on the cars for his family. In that moment he said he saw Margie looking stunning as ever and the in-laws beckoning him to come. He explained to the boys that he needed to go on this journey with them and with that he breathed his last breath. He had gone to be in the arms of his precious Lord and be reunited with his loved ones who preceded him on this journey.

Chapter 21

Loss Shatters Nick's World

A week went by when Nick received an emergency call from his mother that required him to get home as soon as possible. Nick's nuclear family consisted of his parents Kevin and Carol Clarity and their three children, Nick the eldest, his sister Jenny, their baby brother Chris. Sobbing on the phone, his mother explained to Nick that his sister survived an accident the night before. She had been out at the movies and dinner, but on the way home the car she was in was struck head on by a drunk driver. Her boyfriend was propelled through the windshield and killed instantly. Jenny suffered severe injuries. She was in very bad shape. With great concern in Carol's voice, she begged Nick to come home. He quickly made arrangements with work to miss a week and began his drive home.

Pictured above: Marguerite with her first born born son, Anthony. When Anthony reached his teens, the two made a powerful mother and son team for the Kingdom of God.

As he drove, his mind felt overwhelmed by concern for his sister and remembrance days when they were children. Nick and Jenny were the closest in age as there was a little more than a year between their ages. Their little brother came along about eight years later. Jenny grew up as a tomboy so both Nick and she enjoyed the same pastimes. They both enjoyed baseball. She could hit a ball farther than many of the boys her age and of course, everyone wanted her on their team for the sand lot games. Jenny could hit a ball over three houses. After school every day Nick, Jenny, and the gang made their way to the woods behind their house. Deep in the woods, stood a hill with a massive oak tree. A thick rope hung from a large branch. All the children enjoyed taking turns riding the Tarzan Rope. They hopped on at the top of the hill, then they clung to the rope and swung over the hill and flew through the air in sheer pleasure.

How they loved the fresh air and exercise after sitting in school all day long. Simply, it was the best entertainment and a real treat before evening homework. With every passing hour, Nick almost dreaded going home. He did not want to see the hurt in his parents' eyes. He dreaded the deafening silence that awaited him. Jenny, the life of the party, would not be there. He dreaded the steady stream of friends and relations offering their support. He would relish the support but would dread the silence that ultimately follows reporting on Jenny's condition. For the first time in his life, he did not want to go home. With each mile, he felt his nerves tightening in his stomach. He was correct with everything that he feared would happen when he arrived home, but the one thing that he had not prepared himself for was seeing Jenny in the hospital bed with tubes everywhere, lying unconscious. Nick stood silently at her bedside wishing somehow that she would wake up and be the happy, sweet Jenny he had always known, but that did not happen. She just lay there motionless; he could hardly stand it.

In the evening before bed Nick called Lacey to let her know about Jenny's status. Nick told her everything, explaining how she looked and what the doctors were saying. Lacey responded, "Nick, I am so sorry."

Nick added, "It almost feels surreal that any of this has happened." He wished aloud, "I just want her to wake up."

Before they hung up Lacey added, "I will be praying for you and your family."

As Nick sat alone in his room, he felt more alone than ever. She said she would pray for me, for what? He really tried to understand, but he wondered if that could even help. He questioned, "Does she even know me?"

A few days later things took a turn for the worse. The hospital called to say that Jenny was not doing well. All the family needed to go to say their goodbyes. Jenny passed on a late Thursday night. She left this earthly home with her family gathered around. Nick watched as she breathed her last breath. At that moment, his world stopped. As he stood at the bed in stunned silence, he could not understand how everyone outside of that small room still went about their business. People passed outside of Jen's room on their way to visit others while nurses were busy caring for the other patients. For those in that room, time stood still on the pronouncement of Jenny's time of death.

Time still passed even though it seemed to stand still for Nick. He felt crushed. This loss was the worst he had ever experienced and he felt all alone. No one around could help him through this. His parents were unable to help, as they could not even help themselves due to the devastation of Jenny's death. He needed someone to help him through, to hold his hand and heart to walk through this tragedy.

On the day of the funeral, Lacey came to support Nick. He was comforted by having her with him to lean upon. She shared the sorrow but tried to comfort him with the faith she knew. Though Lacey's intentions were good, they made him very angry. After the funeral when they were alone, Nick shared his feelings. He barked at Lacey, "How in the world can you come to this funeral and talk about faith?" He went on, "You know I don't believe in God and you think that someone I don't believe in would comfort me. Sometimes I have no idea where you are coming from." He added in a much louder tone, "You know that if I did believe in Him I would be blaming Him for all this." He asked, "So how could I trust a God who would let this happen?"

Lacey answered, "I understand how upset you feel." "God did not do that to your sister. The drunk driver who hit her did this to her." Nick was so angry that he could not even speak to Lacey at that moment. All the anger and frustration he had been feeling spilled all over Lacey. An ugly argument surfaced and Lacey left for home right away. Nick knew their relationship was over. Their differences in religious beliefs became too much to overcome. He had made his decision and he was going to stick by it.

With the funeral behind him, it was time for Nick to get home and back into his life. As he drove home alone his mind wandered. His thoughts were no longer consumed with Jenny. He was ready to put his grief on the back burner and drive back into his life. He found himself almost feeling relieved that he had the option of leaving his parents' home. He was so tired of constant reminders of Jenny… her things, her pictures, and the sorrow in her parents' eyes that never seemed to let up. He knew it would be hard, but much easier for him to grieve his loss of her and move on. He would always remember Jenny, but he needed to continue living his life, one that no longer included his sister. When he finally reached his destination, he felt totally exhausted. He noticed stacks of mail that begged his attention, but he was too tired.

He went straight to bed and slept well past noon the next day. He woke slowly and lay in bed for a few moments before getting up. While he lay there, he thought of Lacey. He had not seen or heard from her since the funeral. He replayed the terrible fight. He felt bad about it, but she really needed to know where he stood on the matter of faith. He had to do what he did so they could each move on with life. When Monday came, he was more than ready to go back to work. He poured himself into his work. He attacked his assignments with passion as if his work was an outlet for the frustration he felt. At least it all kept his mind busy, so he would not think about Jenny or even Lacey.

Chapter 22

The Last Straw

In early 1970 Richard Nixon presided over our country; people were stressful. In the Chrisagis family stress was also a big issue. In fact, it pulled and molded every member of the family. With everyone busy doing their part to tend to health issues, it was an understatement to say that life was very busy.

Pictured above: John playing with his twin boys, Brian on top of chest and Shawn on the side. Despite John's painful childhood he became a dad to all who knew him.

Anthony John needed glasses. With some curiosity, they traced the eye problem back to his shock of seeing his so-called grandmother, Helena, put his baby brothers in front of an open window. Margie tried to explain things to Anthony so he would never fear this type of thing happening again. Such cruelty seen by a little boy was too difficult for him to understand. John and Margie also had the financial burden of the medical bills, the rearing of three small boys, and his own personal stress. During that time, Helena decided to unleash more cruelty. She called Margie on the phone to sow seeds of doubt and lie about John's faithfulness. Helena was deceitful. She lied about seeing John making out with other women.

Margie listened quietly to the poisonous words that Helena spread through the telephone. The stress of it all took an even greater toll on her health. She kept the things that her mother-in-law told her to herself, eating away at her, further jeopardizing her health.

One night John came home following a very long day of work to find only the boys and Aunt Francie home. Francie explained that she was watching the boys because Margie's parents had to take her to the hospital. Anthony John found her fainted on the floor.

John rushed to the hospital in a panic to find his wife. Greeted by his father-in-law Anthony, John was filled with anger about the stories told by Helena, known by everyone.

Anthony greeted John with two harsh questions, "Where have you been? With your other woman?" John stood in puzzled astonishment at Anthony's greeting, responding, "What are you talking about? I was at work."

"My daughter is my life and if you think you are going to cheat on her or hurt her in any way, I am here to tell you differently. I suggest you get out of her life or I will remove you myself!" Anthony said in a strong voice.

The two started arguing and Carmella jumped up through her tears and said, "Please, Margie can hear this. Stop this now!! We need to think of her. The doctor wants to see you Johnny." John was in shock but said to his mother-in-law, "You of all people know I would never cheat on Margie. You know me. I love her and my kids."

Pictured above:
Anthony DeFilippo loved being a grandfather. Anthony John always watched over his brothers.

Carmie patted John's chest and touched his face with love as tears streamed down her face. Then with that, he walked in to the doctors's office. He could not understand what was going on and asked about his wife's condition. The doctor finally came out to talk to John. He took him aside and explained, "Your wife's health is very fragile, and any stress is not good for her. She told me that your mother has been calling her claiming that you are cheating on her. Now I have known Margie all my life. There was a time when I hoped that she would have become my wife, but she didn't love me, she loved you. You have the perfect wife and mother for your children. What man wouldn't want Margie and what mother-in-law could hate her?"

The doctor went on to share his heart, "I have cared for Margie for a long time as my patient but more importantly as my friend. I need to encourage you to keep your mother in tow and make sure your wife is protected from her. This is serious. The stress your mother is giving your wife is going to kill her. I cannot emphasize this fact enough. This undue stress will kill her; it is just a matter of time. If I were you John, I would get far away from your mother. You will never find a better lady on this planet than Margie. I know. I lost her to you and I have tried to replace her in my heart but can't."

John was shocked. All this was news to him, "Where is my wife? Can I see her?" He had been so busy providing for his family that he failed to keep up on what had been going on with his wife. He felt so bad at his failure that he began to cry. When he finally got into her room, he held her in his arms reassuring her that everything would be okay.

The following day John brought Margie home. John then went so see his mother. He informed her that if she did anything such as this stunt again, he would call the police on her and press charges for harassment. He told her that she could no longer have anything to do with him or his family. He was at the end of his rope and was not going to take it anymore. His mother was in tears and tried to lie about the situation, but John quickly stopped her and said, "Your tears don't affect me anymore mom. Can't you just love my family the way you love my brother Spiro's family? Do you need to make me hate you?" And with that he shut the door on the hate and drama.

In the DeFilippo and Moscato lives, big things happened at the same time John shut the door on his past. Carmie was about to do the same with some of her family. Carmie had two sisters and three brothers. One brother, named Jay, was a saintly man who married and had a sweet family life. Her second brother, named Giacomo, was a devilish rascal who loved women and messed up his life big time. Her third and last brother was Frank, the youngest of the family and one of the kindest and sweetest men ever to walk the earth. He also had a devoted wife with five amazing sons.

One day, Giacomo lay sick in a hospital bed. Carmie rushed to his side. They had not been speaking because Carmie was angry that Giacomo married a second woman without divorcing his first wife. Carmie wanted her brother to live a godly life and wanted better for him. Now with his life almost over, she went to him. When Anthony and Carmie arrived at the hospital, Giacomo was alone in the hospital room. Carmie kissed him and said she loved him. She made her peace with him; Anthony hugged him as well.

Giacomo said to Carmella, "You were always my favorite sister; I loved you more than life itself. You always mothered me and got me out of trouble, but I really messed up my life. It's too late to change things now. Know I love you and I am sorry. I will go to my grave regretting what happened between us."

Carmie cried and said, "Giacomo, I love you. I loved you through each thing you have done and prayed for God to get you out of each problem and guide you."

Giacomo followed up by saying, "Carmie, I was born bad and I think it was because you were born so good that God had no more goodness to put in me." With those words, he shut his eyes as Carmie cried. Anthony hugged his wife. He knew she was heart-broken so he grabbed her and walked her out of the room.

But as Anthony and Carmie walked out the door, they were greeted by Giacomo's two wives and his children. One of the wives, Luisa, was a German woman who was three times the size of Carmie and mean as hell. She jumped at Carmie and started choking her. As Carmie gasped for air, Luisa's huge hands got tighter around her neck. Anthony had to slug Luisa (the over-sized woman) and get her off his sweet wife.

He then asked Luisa, "What is wrong with you? You could have killed my wife!!"

Luisa said, "Carmie has tried to bring Jesus to this family one too many times and I am done with her and her goodness. I want her away from Giacomo!" With that, Carmie and Anthony shut the door on another family member who they loved. This left a big heartache for Carmie who loved her brothers and sisters. She hated to walk away.

Pictured above: Anthony, Shawn and Brian were the closest brothers one could every find. Today, they remain close.

Chapter 23

As the Boys Grew

It's 1976 and Gerald Ford presides over our country. Charlie's Angels were on TV and Rocky was the number one movie. Margie discovered that listening to Christian music brought peace to her home. She started bringing that same music home for her children, ministering to their souls.

The Chrisagis and DeFilippo families settled into what became their normal. Anthony was ten years old and the twins were seven. Brian and Shawn were unable to go to school so they were home-schooled. Michele Vinci taught Anthony in school and always took special care of him. The twins now looked as if they were

malnourished refugees because they grew so slowly, struggling with all their allergies. Doctors called every month to ask about the twins. This caused Margie much stress.

The twins whom doctors claimed would never survive a year were now seven years old because of Margie's love and faith. Doctors kept saying this was a miracle for no child could live like that for seven years. The doctor said it had to be the love in the home that nurtured their lives to bring forth healing. They credited the mother for it all. However, she was slowly

Pictured above: Grandmother Carmie enjoying every moment and always giving her best, especially making clothes for the twins.

dying as well. So much time was spent taking care of her sons that she failed to take care of herself.

Doctor appointments became more frequent as the boys kept passing out from their sickness. Doctors could not believe that these boys were still functioning. The love in the home was felt by all, becoming the twins' life-line. They never realized they were different, but felt loved and normal.

Truth be known most children may be healthy but are starving for love and dying from lack of it but the twins were living proof that "all you need is love" as the line from the famous Beatle's song says.

As time went on Margie's health deteriorated to the point where she needed a wheel chair and constant oxygen. Carmella became full time "Mom" to all. At this time, Margie's doctors claimed she needed a heart transplant, for they could do nothing more to help her condition. However, transplants were extremely dangerous. So, Margie began to see a chiropractor, Dr. Richard Long of Martins Ferry, Ohio, to help relieve her stress.

This man was a born-again Christian and as he worked on her body, he also worked on her soul. He opened the Gospel of the Lord Jesus Christ in a way she had never heard, explaining the need for a Savior to bridge the gap between a Holy God and sinful people. He encouraged her to pray the sinner's prayer with him. She wondered if she needed to do so because she had been in the Catholic church all her life. He tenderly explained, "People can go to church daily, but that doesn't make them a true Christian. It's the same as if someone just stood in a garage believing they were a car. Knowing Him better is a must. If your husband John never asked you to marry him, you could never call yourself his wife. God wants you as His child and wife. You need to marry Him too by receiving His Son as Lord and confessing Him with your mouth. It is a free gift," Dr. Long added.

She understood what he said and finally agreed. They prayed together and Margie became a Christian that day. She felt different because at that instant she submitted her heart to the Lord and something new and wonderful happened. It was a new experience. While she prayed, she felt a power come over her that she could not explain. As Margie prayed in English, suddenly her prayer was in another language. She also felt a peace that surpassed all her understanding. She wanted to remain in that moment, and would have been content to sit right there in the Lord's presence forever.

When they were finished praying, Dr. Long told her about the Full Gospel Business Men's meeting with faith healer Father Michael Scanlan of the Franciscan University in Steubenville, Ohio. The meeting was going to be at Don's Restaurant in Brilliant, Ohio. The Full Gospel Business Men was founded by Demos Shakarian. He began the organization in 1952 when God gave him a vision of millions of men standing shoulder to shoulder praising God. The layman who began the organization struggled through meager beginnings, and in time it did grow to many millions of men across the globe.

When Marguerite arrived home, she told John about everything that happened that pivotal afternoon. Then, she asked John to take her to the Full Gospel meeting with Father Michael. At the meeting, Father Michael spoke of things that were new to Margie and John. He talked of generational curses and healing. With what he shared, the spirit in Margie seemed to wake from a long slumber. She hungered to experience more of God. To say that this meeting would change the lives of the Chrisagis family would be an understatement. She listened intently to every word the Father had to say and when he invited participants to the altar for prayer, Margie was the first there in her wheel chair.

Father Michael just assumed that she went up front to receive prayer for healing her body, but that was not the case. She explained, "I am here for prayer for my two young sons who are dying of allergies." She told him, "I know God is busy and I have lived my life, as I am thirty-two years old. I want to see my sons have the chance to grow up and live their lives."

Smiling in delight at her selflessness, Father Michael replied, "God has plenty of time. He wants to heal you first and then you can go home and pray for your boys." So, he prayed for Margie while John stood in the back of the meeting hall. He prayed that generational curses would be broken seven generations back and thrown into the pit of hell, and that God would heal her to perfect health. He spoke over her heart softly and commanded it to line up with the Word of God.

In no time the woman who needed assistance to breathe took her oxygen off and breathed just fine. Margie then stepped out of her wheelchair. The woman who could not walk a few feet without getting winded ran around the room without tiring at all. As this was going on, in his excitement, John had passed out because he could not believe his eyes! The entire room erupted into thunderous praise to God for what He had done.

When they got home, Margie and Johnny prayed over Brian and Shawn with Nana, Pap and Anthony. She prayed and broke all generational curses off of her children's lives and commanded all evil to get out of her home. While she prayed, she opened the door and demanded every evil spirit leave in the name of Jesus. As she stood holding the door, she felt a spirit push her on the floor as it left.

After that, the twins felt different and their coloring improved. They were no longer pale from their sickness that had bound them for seven years. Both appeared to have more energy. They were healed. So, Margie wanted to take her boys out for a very long overdue family outing. Her boys had never been out of the house to enjoy a meal or even a treat.

John said that this was not wise as they could die if they ate something causing an allergic reaction, not to mention the harm from the sun. He suggested that he and Margie take them to the doctor to have them checked and *then* take them for the treat. Margie insisted they could go to the doctor after the treat because she knew her God had healed her sons completely. John learned from years of experience that when Margie used that tone he would lose the battle, so he gave in and the Chrisagis family went on their first outing as a family. Nana and Pap went with them to celebrate.

So, the seven-year old boys told their mother they wanted to try hot fudge sundaes. They really enjoyed themselves without any ill effects. For the first time, outside in the sun, they were unharmed by its rays. As Margie promised, they then took the boys to the doctor where they were tested for many days. To the doctor's astonishment all the allergies and sickness they had suffered were gone! For the first time in their lives the boys received a clean bill of health. The doctor then examined and tested Margie and her heart. He could hardly believe what he saw!

The doctor asked her to tell him what had happened because he knew her case well. He knew from his training that what he saw was impossible. Her heart was perfectly healthy. It was as if someone had given her a heart transplant.

It was Margie's first opportunity to share what Jesus had done in her life and how he healed her and her boys. He listened to her story with full knowledge of her health. He honestly expected her to be dead by now, not sitting in front of him with a perfectly functioning heart. Because he knew the facts of her health, he knew that something miraculous had in fact happened. Because of this amazing healing, the doctor, a man of the Jewish faith, became a Christian that day.

Her doctor was the first, of many souls she brought to the Lord. Margie spent the rest of her life in service to the Lord, drawing as many people as she could, introducing them to the Lord she loved.

Pictured above:
The first time the twins played outside with their brother.
Shawn, Anthony and Brian.

Father Michael Scanlan and Father Francis MacNutt had Margie travel with them and together they had great healing services all over the Tri-State area. At the time Catholics never let a woman be in a position such as that; yet, they could not deny the anointing and power of God that flowed through Margie.

She appeared on many Christian TV networks, proclaiming and sharing the testimony of the healing that she and her boys received. Using it as a spring board to share the gospel, she wanted everyone to know the love she found in Jesus.

Her love for people and her Lord inspired her to go to her in-laws and share her faith with them. She reassured her mother-in-law Helena that she had forgiven her for all the problems that she caused. Margie encouraged her to ask for forgiveness from God and change her life in Jesus, but Helena refused. In fact, she mocked Margie. So Margie and John left but grieved over this moment. This was the last time John ever saw his mother in her lifetime.

Many turned against Margie for her faith but more followed her and found salvation, deliverance and healing through Christ. People sought out Margie and came from all over the United States to see this amazing and anointed woman of God. When she prayed, miracles took place. She saw people with cancer healed, she raised the dead, she saw tumors dissolve, and she saw legs grow and eyes see again. The miracles that took place through Marguerite DeFilippo Chrisagis was not Margie, but her faith in what Jesus did for her and her family. She knew He would do the same for everyone. She knew He was no respecter of persons. Hebrews 13:8 in the Bible says, "Jesus Christ the same yesterday, and today, and forever

Chapter 24

The Letter

It had been more than a few weeks since Nick's family laid his sister Jenny to rest. Nick tossed himself into his work and life to lessen the pain of her death. It had been a hard adjustment with grief spilling out at any time. He worked hard to keep to his normal routine, but something reminded him of Jenny, causing him to fall back into grief. When the waves of grief hit, he found it hard to concentrate. He kept working as this comforted him even if he was unable to totally focus.

He kept busy with work during the day and research on the DeFilippo and Chrisagis families after work. At night, he spent his time sorting through piles of mail that had come in while he went home for the funeral. At first, he quickly organized them in order of importance. He knew bills needed to be paid first, so he tackled them by putting the other envelopes aside. As he worked at the beginning of his grief, he spent many evenings going to bed early because he found the work of grief ever so tiring.

Pictured above:
Little Anthony with Pap, Shawn
on Pap's back and Brian on Dad's back.

As time went on, he was able to sleep less and started getting back to himself. Not normal as it was but a normal that circumstances redefined.

One evening he sat while going through the cards and letters, reading each one, thinking of the person who sent it and finding comfort in the kind words. It was as though those cards and notes were arms wrapped around him. He went through several envelopes that evening and became tired, so he decided that the next one would be the last before he retired to bed. He picked up the envelope and noticed that the return address was his parents' house with Jenny's name in the corner. He sat holding the envelope almost afraid to open it. Apparently, she wrote it three days before her accident. It took him a while to open it but when he finally did, he found a hand-written letter and a small book. The book was titled Forgive Me For Waiting So Long to Tell You This. He set the book aside and read the note.

My Dearest Nick,

Something has happened to me that I need to share it with you. Do you remember when we were little, and Mom used to call us "Salt and Pepper" because we were so close that we shared everything? There were no secrets between us. I wanted you to be the first to know of the life-changing experience I just had.

As you know, the last few years of my life can best be summed up in one word and that word is struggle. It has been hard since my relationship with Toby ended. I really did not see any of that coming because Toby and I were so well-matched just like you and I, salt and pepper. I still find it hard to believe that he called the wedding off the way he did. A week before the nuptials he disappeared. He only left a note saying he could not do this anymore. I could not see how he could do this when we fit together so well. We had the same views, the same goals. We worked well together. I was not happy when he dropped the bomb that turned my life upside down. After the breakup, the work to cancel the wedding, return the gifts, and cancel honeymoon plans kept me busy for a while. I found myself in despair when all the work of dismantling the wedding had finally reached an end. I wondered, not only what I would do with my life, but I found I lost my purpose. I felt stuck not knowing how I ended up where I landed. I was to be Mrs. Toby Anderman, but with the status of wife stripped from me I was lost, and I could no longer find my place. It was at my lowest point that I realized my purpose is much bigger than just me. Just when I needed it most, a friend from college sent me the book that I have enclosed for you. In that little book I learned so much. It is a wonderful read that teaches the reader the gospel in simple terms. In that beautiful little book, I met a Savior. A gentle King who I made the Lord of my life.

Man is born with a natural desire to know God. To make it possible for a sinful man to have a relationship with a Holy God there needs to be a mediator. This is where Jesus comes in. Jesus is the perfect Son of God. God sent His only Son to earth to die for mankind. The sin of man was put on the Cross to make it possible for man to be in a relationship with a Holy God.

I asked Jesus into my heart. You probably do not know this, but God's greatest desire is a relationship with His creation. I started this journey with a prayer asking Jesus to show Himself to me. To be honest, I did not know if He was real. So, I asked Him to show me if He was real and He did. The only logical response to this was to accept Him as Lord and Savior of my life. For the first time in my life, I have found peace with the understanding that God has my purpose in His hands.

Pictured above: Shawn, Anthony DeFilippo, Brian and Anthony with their grandfather. Top row: Carmella, Margie and John.

Nick, I am not with you now, but I know you well enough to know how you look right now. Your face has a puzzled look on it and you are dumb struck at my revelation. I can bet you are very confused and angry. Nick, please see past your feelings and hear my words. I challenge you to read the book and see for yourself that Jesus is real. I love you and want you to meet my Lord and Savior."

Nick could not believe what he just read. What happened to his sister? This was not the cautious level-headed girl who he once knew.

Jen continued, "It is just like a relationship with anyone else. This whole thing was not at all what I thought it was. It is not a religion, it is a relationship. It is not a church but a living body of believers. It is not a story, it is a testimony. It is not just a lesson, it is a life style. Nick, the truth of the matter is that Christianity is nothing like I thought it was. It is not pious people pretending to be perfect. It is imperfect people putting their lives into the hands of a Holy God. I hope you can accept my decision to become a disciple of Jesus. If you do decide to reject me because of my faith then so be it. I want you to know you are forgiven. There is something I need to say to you, and honestly, I do not know why. But for some reason you need to hear this. No one ever has any right to be angry with God. Whatever is to come, please don't be angry with God. I challenge you Nick to do your own search and learn for yourself that Jesus is real. Seek Him and ask Him to show Himself to you. If He is not real what will you lose? If you find Him real, you have so much more to gain.

I love you Nick!

Your sister,
(the Salt to your Pepper)
Jenny

Nick picked up the book that Jenny sent and read it from cover to cover. In this little book he learned who God is, what His standards are, how much He loves people and all that He has done for people. He learned that through repentance and faith we can find God. After contemplating all that he read, Nick decided to pray for the first time in his life. He had to know if God was real or not. He prayed the following prayer:

"Lord, I don't know what to say. I realize how funny that is, a man who puts words on paper for a living cannot find the words to pray. I have seen miracles that have been credited to You. I have seen people who cling to you in faithful devotion, but I have no idea if You are real. I have never prayed before, so I am not sure if I am doing this right or not, but here goes. I know that I am a selfish sinner but what I do not know is, are You real? Please show me if You are real, teach me and guide me."

Pictured above top row from left to right: Anthony, Brian and Shawn. Bottom row: John, Margie and Carmie with dogs Chewie and Han Solo.

After Nick prayed, he got on the Internet and looked up the Chrisagis Brothers tour dates, to find where they would be ministering next. He marked it down on the calendar and made plans to be in the audience. The following week, Nick went to the Chrisagis Brothers concert and asked to have an interview with the famous brothers he was getting to know from all the many stories he heard and had became obsessed with. Now he would finally know the rest of the story:

Chapter 25

Three Healings, Life and Faith Altered

Since the healings of Brian and Shawn Chrisagis to say that life changed would be a serious understatement. Because of the miracle, the boys are able to enjoy all kinds of foods. They can get out of the house without harm by the sun. At the beginning, for these two little seven-year-olds it was as if they stepped into a whole new world, one that others take for granted.

But for these children, everything was new and exciting. They went to the park for the first time in their lives and had fun playing and exploring. The first seven years of life, they had never entered a grocery store. They had never seen anything like it. It gave the Chrisagis family freedom as never before. With numerous appointments with doctors no longer taking their time the family had time to do things together. This was all so amazing and life-changing in and of itself, but add to that the healing of Marguerite.

This family underwent what could best be described as revolutionary. The woman who had been so close to death's door was revitalized with health and vitality.

Margie's life was altered as her energy was renewed so she could be the mother she was unable to be during sickness. It was a whole new life for this family. Marguerite had always had a heart for prayer since being a small child. Since the day at the Chiropractor's office

Pictured above Shawn on bottom and Brian sitting up higher in their famous promo picture.

when she was saved and filled with the Holy Spirit and with this impartation, her prayers had power behind them, guided by the Holy Spirit. The Holy Spirit always spoke to her as she prayed.

One time in prayer the Holy Spirit told her about a young lady named Marsha, whose mother-in-law planned to kill her and her child. God told Margie that the young woman would call her and when she said, "It is time" that was her sign to go and collect them, protecting them from harm. It happened just as God said. Margie and John went and picked Marsha and the baby up when the call came in.

Later that night Marsha's husband came home and found his mother with a knife in her. He took her to a hospital where she confessed. She planned to kill Marsha and their child along with killing herself. Sam had to put his mother in mental health care for her mental illness, so she could no longer harm anyone again. He was so thankful to Margie for saving his wife and child.

In prayer, Margie was very faithful. When the Lord instructed, she prayed for all who He told her to even if she did not know them. In the quiet solitude of her prayer closet in 1979 God told her to pray for a man in a desperate situation. The man's name was Jack Scalia. She had no idea he was internationally known as a top male model, and that he had also been named one of the sexiest men at the time. During his success he found himself floundering in a sea of personal problems.

From the world's standards he seemed to have it all. He had a successful career, and he was one of the world's best-looking men. Women longed to be with him and men wanted to be him, but there was an intense disconnect coupled with a drug problem he found himself in at the end. While Margie prayed in her prayer closet in 1979 Jack was on the thirteenth story of a building in Munich, Germany.

Rather than sitting comfortably in his room, he was on the ledge. He had had enough of all the struggles, addiction, self-loathing, and relationships with the hottest women for whom he found himself in bondage. So his plan was to end his suffering. While out on that ledge, Jack heard the voice of God. He heard the voice of God promise that if he got back inside the hotel room that his life would change.

He did follow the instructions and at that moment his agent called and told him that he had gotten Jack into rehab. While in rehab, he got involved in the New Age Movement. Margie still prayed for him for years. Jack had become one of Hollywood's most bankable movie stars and leading actors with TV Series like *The Devlin Connection, Hollywood Beat, Dallas, Remington Steele, "Wolf", "Tequila and Bonetti, Pointman* and *All My Children*. He also starred in over fifty films with legendary beauties and actresses such as Farrah Fawcett, Raquel Welch, Bo Derek, and others. He was in nearly every Jackie Collins film. He also was voted one of the most handsome men in history by *TV Guide*, plus *People* Magazine named him one of the Sexiest Men in the world past and present. He had it all in the world's eyes. He had everything except Jesus.

Then the Lord told Margie to have her twins make a website for Jack and buy the domain name. She said to leave the family phone number on the website so he will call us when he sees it. She said God told her that he will call and that he will be saved. When Jack discovered this website, he called the phone number that appeared on the site. He was upset, wondering who had given the permission to use his domain name. The twins explained to him about the years that their mom had been praying for him. He knew it was God when they told him that her prayers for him had started in 1979 and at that time, they were intense. They went on and said she had the entire family praying for him that day and every day following. He was amazed because at this time he was at his lowest. Jack wanted to meet the entire family in California, and so the family went out to meet him.

Jack and the Chrisagis family had the opportunity to meet and develop a strong relationship. That day Jack received Jesus as Lord over his life and he became a son to Margie and John. Scalia became the fourth son, and a brother to all three Chrisagis boys. He also became a grandson to Nana. He came and stayed at their home every month and called it his home. Jack credited this special lady's faithfulness that reached down and grabbed him out of the gates of hell and placed him into the loving arms of his precious Lord and Savior. Margie, a total stranger, gave him a gift, the ultimate gift. Why did she do that? Because she gave it all to Jesus and through her, He gave it all back to Jack and many others.

Many stars came to Christ through Margie and her family's prayers simply because she remained faithful to hear God's sweet voice tell her when they needed Him the most. God told her to pray for legendary Cover-Girl Model/Actress Jennifer O'Neill who starred in feature films such as *Summer of 42*, *Rio Lobo*, and *Scanners*. Her face launched thousands of beauty magazines. She was named by beauty experts as one of the greatest beauties of all time. When God told Margie to pray for Jennifer it was at one of the worst times of her life.

Jennifer came to know the Lord after many marriages and horrific tragedies. O'Neill also became flesh and blood to the Chrisagis family. They raised her up in the Lord and now she is one of the greatest Christian speakers in the world. The Chrisagis Twins were her personal assistants for eighteen years. She is also a spokesperson against abortion. She helps Veterans with her Horse Ranch called "Hillenglade", and is the face of Christians in the Christian movie Industry.

In fact, Jack Scalia was the last soul Margie introduced to Jesus before God called her to Heaven for eternity. It is kind of neat to think how God orchestrated Marguerite's life. She was supposed to die from her heart, yet her heart was the thing that pumped with God and touched all lives from a small town called Yorkville, Ohio to Hollywood, California and even Munich, Germany. This lady touched the world for Jesus.

Before she died, she had two strokes at the age of fifty-three that left her almost in a vegetative state, but her family nursed her back to health. The doctors said she would never walk, talk, or function again but they were wrong. God brought her through and the doctors stood amazed. Her family worked around the clock as caregivers.

Her son, Anthony, and her mother Carmella stayed with her round the clock getting her back up and strong again. Some of Margie's greatest moments in ministry happened in those years, seeing the celebrities come to Christ. At fifty-nine she fought breast cancer and overcame it for five years. In those years Johnny and the twins worked hard to find cures for her. They traveled all over the world to get medicines from other counties. Actress Jennifer O'Neill and Actor Jack Scalia also tried to find cures to help the family. Even actor Efrem Zimbalist heard about this beautiful lady and sent boxes of health food products to save this amazing woman of God, but at age sixty-four she succumbed to brain cancer. Jack came to the funeral and gave his story. He called her "Mom" because she cared enough to love him and save his life. After that, Jack joined the Chrisagis Brothers in ministry. They traveled together throughout the United States for two years and touched many for Jesus.

Chapter 26

A Tombstone with Two Dates Explained

Years passed all too quickly and the DeFilippo and Chrisagis families remained strong as they reared three healthy boys. The reality of life was filled with both good and bad years. With her boys' new-found health and her perfectly functioning heart, Margie was off to the races with more energy than she had in a long time. She dove into caring for her little family. She worked hard to meet their physical, emotional, and spiritual needs. In her gratitude to her Lord she shared His love and her healing with anyone who would take time to listen.

Pictured above: Anthony and Carmella DeFilippo lived an upstanding life of integrity. A true example of true Christian living.

It started off small but soon the ministry God gave her was booked weekly in churches, conferences, Women's Aglow and more. She always traveled with John as the driver, and her three sons, who always sang before she ministered. They saw great miracles and deliverance take place in each meeting. The result of her relationship with her Lord was an intense hunger for the Word and prayer. The fruit of her passion for her Lord was lost souls. Her warm and inviting personality coupled with her passion made her a magnet for those who were hungry and seeking.

On her knees, her boys learned how to seek and follow hard after God. Each grew to be godly men. All three sons are now serving in music ministry and children's ministry. John and Margie were so proud. As time went on Margie stepped down to make her three sons become the ministers God called them to be in this life. She taught them how to minister and she gave them a strong foundation in knowing the Word of God. They traveled all over the states with their three sons, so the sons could sing and minister for the Lord.

Life was perfect and their teenage sons never fought or rebelled. The three sons wanted to live for the Lord and they were happy and blessed to have such godly parents. They listened to only Christian music and were inspired by artists such as Stephanie Boosahda, Farrell & Farrell, Scott Wesley Brown, Russ Taff, Sandi Patty, Evie Tornquist, Larnelle Harris, Michael English, Carman, Phil Driscoll, Rambo/McGuire, Dave Boyer, Andréa Crouch and more. They sat under those anointed musical artists and prayed for that same anointing. God started pouring out His spirit on these three young men and they were amazed at how God used them all.

Time passed, and life moved with a steady rhythm that kept everything humming. That is until one day the rhythm was shattered by tragedy. All the children were high schoolers, so gone were the days of toys and young lives filled with imagination. Now the days were filled with matters that were important to young men as they sought God to find their place

Pictured at left:
John and Marguerite Chrisagis have gone on to Glory, but their sons remain to continue their legacy. These two remarkable people changed lives worldwide because of Margie's obedience to God. Priests, Nuns and Hollywood stars came to honor the life she lived.

as they stepped into adulthood. The young men were dating and trying to live for the Lord and do His will. Life unfolded in a new rhythm, a mature rhythm when one day it all changed.

It is amazing how life can change in just one minute. Without rhyme, reason or warning. It can become totally altered forever.

That fateful morning the house was filled with the active preparation for the boys to get to school. Carmella found Anthony on the floor not breathing and without a pulse. She screamed and screamed. Apparently, Anthony had fallen backwards with his walker and hit the bedroom dresser and broke his neck. As Carmie screamed for help, John ran in and checked his vitals, he was dead. So John called 911. An ambulance came and the paramedics worked on Anthony DeFilippo for 15 minutes without any sign of life. His eyes were back in his head, the blood had dried up, his coloring was gray and pasty, and his skin was that of a corpse.

Margie had just picked up her sons from school and as she walked through the door she felt overwhelmed with grief. She could not believe her eyes. Her hero, her role model, her dad was dead. Her sons ran to their Nana and held her as she cried in terror. John went to hug Margie but instantly the Holy Spirit fell on her and told her to speak her dad's spirit back into his body and command the spirit of death out of him and away from the house.

She spoke in strong authority almost in a voice different from her own. It was as if God was speaking through her as she sent satan out of the house. As she did, her father started coughing up blood and his eyes came back into the sockets, he started bleeding again and he tried to get up. The paramedics jumped back and shook as they tried to get away from him. John jumped down and said, "Don't try to get up, we don't want anything broken. Let them help you up."

But the paramedics looked even more pale then Anthony DeFilippo. They worked on him a little then sat him up so they could get him to the hospital. But his neck was twisted in some horrific form unlike anything imaginable. The paramedics tried to work on it and then God spoke to Margie and she did exactly as He instructed. She held her hand behind his head and said, "Line up with the Word of God! Be made whole!!" And she watched along with all who stood watching. The neck was made whole again as they heard it crack and move into place.

One of the paramedics was so astonished and choked up that he said, "Lady, you scare the hell out of us. But whatever power you have works. In all my days, I have never witnessed anyone like you. Are you a witch or something? I want you to be around me if I am ever in trouble. Your father was dead for 25 to 30 minutes and now he is alive." Margie shook, and Johnny held her and kissed her. Carmella started hugging and kissing her husband and praising the Lord.

At the time, Anthony DeFilippo was now in his late sixties and life had taken its toll on his body. The man who once stood straight and strong was now hunched over. His legs could scarcely support his body. Those legs that once ran and played were failing him. He was in constant pain and many times wished for a way out of it all. Pain is exhausting, and Anthony just wanted rest from it. He was a man of faith, so he knew where he would go after his death and he had come to the point where he was looking forward to going home. In Heaven he would have a healthy body, one without pain.

Because of all that had taken place that morning the paramedics urged them to allow them to take Anthony to get checked at the hospital. So, they did and a few hours later, the man who had been dead walked out of the hospital under his own power. It was a glorious day and the family kept thanking God. That day it was not medicine or CPR that saved Anthony, it was prayer and Margie's ability to hear the voice of God.

The family rejoiced at the faithfulness of their Lord and Savior. With thankful hearts they praised the God they loved. Days later, Anthony shared what he had experienced when he was dead. He said that he was in a most peaceful place, somewhere he had never been. He said that he walked across fields covered in flowers. When he stepped on a cluster of these flowers, they were not trampled under his feet, but they bounced back up straight, tall and unharmed after being stepped on.

He talked about how he was young and healthy again and that he saw and talked to Jesus. He said it was so beautiful, but he could not see Jesus' face because His face was so glorious. But he saw the nail scars in His hands and feet. Jesus showed him his mansion and he saw horses. Then Jesus told him it wasn't his time and that he had to return to his family, so they knew that Heaven was real. Because the DeFilippo and Chrisagis families were once strong Catholics they needed to know that people who die don't wait in purgatory, but they go straight to Heaven or hell according to how they lived their lives.

Anthony often said that he wished he could be back there now and made it sound as if he were disappointed to be back in his old body. He was just so tired and worn down.

There are times in life when we can clearly see that all good things must come to an end.

Anthony cried out nightly, "Father, I hurt! Help me!" Margie saw that her father suffered so she cried and prayed again that the Lord would remove her father's suffering. God spoke to her in a sweet voice and told her that He could do nothing because Margie stood on His Word and held God to His promises that are found in His Word. She asked what He meant. He spoke again saying that she always quoted the scripture over her family's life, which is, Psalm 90:10 (New Living Translation) "Seventy years are given to us! Some even live to eighty."

God then told her He could not break His promises, due to covenant with His people. He said that she had to break the covenant and ask for God's will to be done for her dad. She argued with God a bit and said, "How can I lose my dad twice? Why did you send him back to let me go through this again?"

God said, "You needed to know that scripture is real, that heaven is eternal, and this life is temporal and that I am faithful to the faithful." Therefore, with that Margie and her mom sat together and talked. They both prayed God's will to be done. It was not long after that when Anthony finally passed into his reward. This time the family was ready, they were broken over the loss, but they were ready because it was what was best for Anthony. They had peace as they grieved their loss. They were comforted in the fact that it was not goodbye, but I will see you in glory. Until we meet again in the presence of the Lord." That was a day that they could all look forward to with anticipation.

So, Nick had finally found the answer to the question for which he had searched a very long time. He finally learned why two sets of dates appeared on the tombstone. Anthony DeFilippo was born, died, and was brought back to life from death. It was his daughter, Margie, who insisted that the two sets of dates be put on his tombstone when he did finally move to glory.

Many of the stories of the DeFilippo and the Chrisagis families had touched Nick very deeply. In a small way, the stories had changed him forever. The answer to the first question he asked

touched him deeper than any of the others. He worked hard and found the answer. Though the answer left him with more questions than he could imagine. He finally realized that he was only passing through and life is just the small portion in God's plan for eternity. He realized he had to really begin a new life and chapter with Lacey by his side.

Pictured above:
Anthony Chrisagis sang in the Night Clubs and Concert Halls in Las Vegas. He also traveled throughout London singing the songs of Frank Sinatra, Dean Martin and Elvis Presley. This is his publicity photo for these concerts.

Chapter 27

Nick's Big Decision

It had been more than a month since Jenny's funeral when Nick had been in touch with Lacey. She knew he was going through some major life changes and to support him she gave him time and space to deal with his grief. Of course, she prayed for him during this time.

One night he showed up at her apartment, very nervously clutching flowers. After he walked up to the door he stood in front of it for more than a few minutes, gathering the courage to knock on the door. Nick knew that what he had to tell her would be difficult. He worried about how she might respond. Finally, he gathered the courage and he knocked on the door waiting for her answer.

Lacey answered the door, surprised to see Nick. Lacey questioned with shock in her voice, "Nick, so nice to see you. How are you doing?"

Nick shyly answered, "I am okay, how are you?"

Lacey responded, "I am fine. Can I help you with something?"

Nick nervously responded, "Do you have time to talk?"

Lacey responded, "Sure, come in."

She escorted him to the couch where they sat together. Lacey could tell that Nick had something on his mind but was having trouble getting it out. As they caught up on news she asked him questions that she knew would be easy for him to answer. She asked, "How is work? I read the article you wrote about the opioid epidemic. It was so informative and compassionate."

Nick responded, "Thank you, I am glad you enjoyed it."

Finally, after small talk, Nick got to the purpose of his visit. "Lacey, I need to apologize for the way I behaved at Jen's funeral," he said. "There was no excuse for treating you the way I did. I wanted to thank you for giving me time after the funeral to be alone in my grief."

Lacey added, "Time does heal all wounds and I am happy that you are feeling better."

Nick responded, "Thank you. You are very right. Can I tell you what has happened to me while we were apart?"

"Ok", said Lacey.

"I need to tell you how sorry I am. Since we had gotten together, I have been making fun of your faith. I thought it simple, a crutch. In my misunderstanding, I thought you less than myself because you had faith and I did not. I am so sorry for mistreating you."

"Thank you for apologizing and you are forgiven." Lacey responded. "What changed your mind and your attitude?"

He explained, "After the funeral when I finally had the energy to get back into life, I found a letter that Jenny wrote just days before her accident. With the letter she enclosed a small book called, Forgive Me for Waiting So long to Tell You This. In her letter she laid out God's plan for salvation and her testimony. It was about this time that all the pieces came together with the DeFilippo and Chrisagis family stories. With all the pieces of the puzzle in place who could help but to believe. Who can witness seasons of miracles and not be moved?

They were incredible people, a beautiful mixture of average and extraordinary all wrapped into one. They co-existed in a way that one cannot help but to be drawn to them and their story. Their simple grace, all that they dealt with, and the fact that they came through in victory stirs in one a longing to have what they have and know the God they know."

He added in a very serious tone, "I had to know if God was real, so I prayed and asked that He show Himself to me. He showed Himself to me in a big way." They sat silently for a while and finally Nick broke it with the announcement, "Lacey, I am a Christian, your brother in Christ."

Lacey smiled so sweetly. He went on, "Lacey, it is like in the space of one day I woke up to a whole different world. Everything is so new. Now I know this life isn't perfect and I am surely not. But I know I am in the hands of One who is perfect. He is my Savior but more importantly, He is my Lord. My desire is to seek Him, know Him fully, and obey what He wants me to do with my life."

He held out the bouquet of flowers that he had been playing with the whole time they were talking. As he held out the flowers, he asked, "Lacey, will you walk with Jesus with me?"

Lacey melted into his arms and cried at the request. Her heart's desire had unfolded in such a beautiful way. She dreamed of finding a man who would share Jesus with her, walking daily in His will. Through tears she responded, "Yes, I would love to take your hand and walk with Jesus with you." She looked up to the Heavens and added, "Thank you, Lord."

In Revelation 12:11 the Scripture tells us that they will be won by the word of their testimony. Victory won over satan because of the Blood of the lamb and the word of their testimony. So, it was for Nick. Most of the people who were part of the DeFilippo and Chrisagis testimony have gone home to be with their Lord, but their testimony will live on for years to come, drawing all who hear it to God. Giving glory

Pictured above: The Chrisagis Brothers (Brian and Shawn) are still ministering full time worldwide and working on many new TV and Music projects they hope will keep changing lives and bringing hope through God's love. They feel their parents and grandparents cheering them on in the journey that lie ahead.

to their Lord and Savior, Jesus. They truly have left "A Legacy of Love" for us all to follow.

Prayer for Salvation

Dear Lord,

I admit that I am a sinner. I have done many things that did not please You. I have lived my life for myself only. I am sorry, and I repent. I ask you to forgive me.

I believe that You died on the Cross for me, to save me. You did what I could not do for myself. I come to You now and ask You to take control of my life; I give it to You. From this day forward, help me to live every day for You and in a way that pleases You.

I love You, Lord, and I thank You that I will spend all eternity with you. Amen.

About the Author

Debbie Fuller spent 20 plus years home schooling her three children who are now successful adults in their respective field of study. Debbie also served as a missionary with *Hope for the Family* in Romania. She is a free lance writer who has worked for Christian Hollywood. Fuller has written a number of books and is currently working on a blog for Linked in Learning. By far the most rewarding and exciting thing Fuller has done thus far with her gift for writing is having the opportunity to write The Chrisagis Brothers family story with them. In writing this book she found healing for herself. Debbie prays that all who read it will find that same healing through Christ.

About the Co-Authors

Brian and Shawn Chrisagis are identical twins who were never to be born. Their life changing testimony and ministry of 35 years travels the world.

They have appeared on every Christian Network and had their own TV series, radio shows, and TV specials.

The brothers are best known as recording artists who have been nominated for many awards and won as the best duo in Christian Music by the *Extraordinary People Awards*. They have created their own events such as *Legends in Christian Music*, *All That Glitters* Conferences, and *Hollywood Legends* events.

The Chrisagis Brothers are ordained ministers, portrait and cartoon artists, models and actors.

Visit www.chrisagisbrothersministries.org to learn more.

Pictured: The Chrisagis Brothers (Brian above, Shawn at right). Both publicity photos were for the *Saved by the Brothers* TV reality series that was done by A&E.

About the Publisher

RPJ & Company began publishing Christian and other inspirational books following the Spirit's leading with Romans 14:17 as its foundation in 2004. We work with pastors, leaders, ministers, missionaries and others with messages to help the Body of Christ. Our published books continue to empower, inspire and motivate people to aspire to a higher level of understanding through the written word.

RPJ & Company is dedicated to assisting those individuals who desire to publish books that are uplifting, inspiring and self-help in nature. We also offer assistance for those who would like to self publish.

The special service that we provide is customized, quality layout and design for every client. This gives first time authors a chance at becoming successfully published. For every book, we offer exposure and a worldwide presence to market the book. We help new authors become discovered!

"As an author and publisher, I can guide you through the steps of creating, editing, proofreading while providing professional quality layout and design. The finished book will be one in which you will be proud to share."

- Kathleen Schubitz
Founder and CEO

A few of our popular books:

    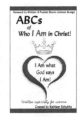

54245080R00083

Made in the
USA
Lexington, KY